MW00339548

TIMES TABLES THE FUN WAY

TEACHER'S MANUAL

Second Edition - Revised

© 1995

Key Publishers, Inc.
Sandy, Utah

ISBN 1-883841-32-1

Written By: Judy Rodriguez

TIMES TABLES THE FUN WAY

TEACHER'S MANUAL

Second Edition

COPYRIGHT © 1995

BY KEY PUBLISHERS, INC.

All rights reserved. Printed in the United States of America. Pages which bear the "may be copied" insignia, may be reproduced for classroom use. No other part of this book may be used or reproduced in any manner without written permission except in the case of reprints in the context of reviews.

FOR INFORMATION WRITE:
KEY PUBLISHERS, INC.,
6 SUNWOOD LANE
SANDY, UTAH 84092

1-801-572-1000

Copyright © 1994, 1995
First Printing 1994
Second Printing 1995, Second Edition
Third Printing 1996, Second Edition
Fourth Printing 1997, Second Edition

ISBN 1-883841-32-1

Attention: Schools and Businesses
Times Tables the Fun Way Teacher's Manual is available at quantity discounts with bulk purchase for educational, business, or sales promotional use.

NOTE TO TEACHERS

Times Tables the Fun Way is a picture and story method of learning the times tables. Students enjoy the variety and range of activities that are possible with the story method. The Teacher's Manual should be used in conjunction with the *Times Tables the Fun Way* Book for Kids (Student Text), *Times Tables the Fun Way* Student Workbook, and *Times Tables the Fun Way* Flash Cards. The Teacher's Manual contains detailed lesson plans, games, game cards, grading templates, and awards. The lesson plans present the stories in an order for most effective learning. After each lesson a game may be played to reinforce the facts presented. The workbook pages correlate to the lesson plans and should be presented in the outlined order.

The success of this method depends on adequate practice in applying the stories to the raw fact. Studies have shown that students who learn with the picture - story method retain the facts for longer periods and score higher on post-tests because the facts are firmly implanted in long term memory. In the early learning phases, it will be necessary to give story clues to students in order to trigger the answers to the facts. Once the stories are thoroughly learned and practiced with the workbook and text, students will by-pass the story when remembering the fact. So, the stories are an intermittent, but crucial phase of learning the multiplication facts by the picture and story method.

Each lesson is divided into short mini lessons. If students are being introduced to the times tables for the first time, they should be taught one mini lesson per day, ideally, two days per week. Duration of each lesson is approximately 60 to 90 minutes, or 15 - 30 minutes for the mini lessons. The *Times Tables the Fun Way* system is designed as an introduction to times tables for 2nd or 3rd graders, but it can also be used in special education programs and in the higher grades for review or learning of the more difficult or forgotten facts. Students who are reviewing their times tables can be taught an entire lesson in one session, (several mini lessons). For 2nd or 3rd graders, the *Times Tables the Fun Way* Picture Method should be the student's first exposure to times tables and followed by the grade level mathematics text. After mastery of times tables has been achieved, students will be able to enjoy applying their newly learned facts to additional basic math skills.

Have fun teaching. We are sure that you and your students will enjoy learning *Times Tables the Fun Way*.

DESCRIPTION OF *TIMES TABLES THE FUN WAY*
WORKBOOK MATERIALS

Student Questionnaire:
The questionnaire is used to stimulate discussion. It starts the program with a personal and fun activity.

Pre-test:
The pre-test is timed for 6 minutes and used as a baseline to measure progress against the post-test. It contains 48 facts, some zeroes and all of the ones through nines, but no reversals, i.e. 7 x 6 but not 6 x 7. The commutative property is explained in the *Times Tables the Fun Way* Text.

Quizzes:
Quizzes are given at the start of each lesson. They are used to reinforce the stories by asking the students to draw a picture or write the story. This strengthens the connection between the story and the fact. It is always better to review the stories or give hints during the quiz, if necessary, than to leave the quiz section blank. Students learn by re-telling or drawing the picture of the story. The quiz has two parts. The upper portion is a test of the raw facts and the lower portion tests the student's memory of the stories. The story section should be marked correct if the students show any indication that they have remembered the correct story for that fact.

Timed Practice Sheets:
These sheets are timed and used to practice the ones, twos, fives, and nines. Students should write down the time it took them to complete the page. The goal is for students to improve their own times and scores on each type of Timed Practice Sheet. For example: The Ones and Twos Practice Sheet should get faster each time it is taken. However, the Fives Practice Sheet time should not be faster than the Ones and Twos because the Fives are harder. The Fives Practice Sheet Time should be faster than the last time the student took the Fives Practice Sheet.

Worksheets:
These are used to practice the introduced facts. Each worksheet contains only the facts that have been introduced so far. Students will learn to do two digit by one digit multiplication. At this stage, learning to add and multiply in the same problem adds diversity to times tables practice. The workbook pages go through a step by step explanation of two digit by one digit multiplication as well as simple division and learning the nines.

Post-test:
The post-test is timed for 6 minutes. The goal is for the students to score 100% on the post-test. The average score at the end of the 8 hour program in a workshop setting has been 97%.

Other Activity Sheets:
Homework Test: Students should take the graded test and learn the missed facts for homework. The Homework Quiz is given at the next lesson and will test the students on the facts that were missed on the Homework Test.
Crossword Puzzle: Facts are given as clues and students must fill in the key words of the story. This can be played in a group format or done individually.

DESCRIPTION OF WORKBOOK MATERIALS CONTINUED:

Stamp and Score Summary Sheet:

Students are able to map their progress by filling out their Quiz scores and Timed Practice scores and times. There is a square at the bottom of the sheet to put a stamp or a sticker when the indicated goals are reached. Students should be rewarded after each lesson for improving scores, receiving 100%, winning at the games, or completing worksheet pages.

SKILLS COVERED IN THE STUDENT WORKBOOK

Multiplication Facts: 0 - 12

Double Digit By Single Digit Multiplication

Double Digit By Single Digit Multiplication With Carrying

Simple Division

Memorizing the facts and rehearsing them over and over can be boring and tedious for students. When new, but simple skills are introduced during the facts learning process, students are able to apply their newly learned facts to varied operations. This teaches students how they will be using their multiplication facts while reinforcing the newly learned facts. When students encounter these skills in their grade level text book, they will already have been introduced to them, making the learning process easier and more enjoyable.

MEMORIZING THE TENS, ELEVENS, AND TWELVES

The *Times Tables The Fun Way* Method teaches students to memorize the facts, ones through the nines. Students are taught double digit multiplication in the second lesson and can easily figure out the answers for the 10's, 11's, and 12's. It is not necessary to have these facts memorized in order to do higher grade level skills like fractions, division, and decimals. Therefore, we do not feel that it is necessary to memorize these double digit facts.

DESCRIPTION OF *TIMES TABLES THE FUN WAY*
BOOK FOR KIDS

Times Tables the Fun Way Book is in full color and printed on heavy, durable pages. The text covers the zeroes through the nines. All facts for the threes, fours, sixes, sevens, and eights are taught with pictures and stories. Numerical tricks are used to teach the zeroes, ones, twos, fives, and nines. Each fact is addressed once and not taught in reverse order.

DESCRIPTION OF *TIMES TABLES THE FUN WAY*
FLASH CARDS

The flash cards are an integral part of the picture story method. The cards for the story facts show the number characters as well as the raw numbers. The characters with the numbers help the students make the story / fact connection. The number at the bottom right corner of the card represents the lesson that the fact is introduced. The cards can be sorted and used in the order of presentation.

DESCRIPTION OF *TIMES TABLES THE FUN WAY* - POSTERS

The posters will enhance retention when used as a visual aid while teaching the stories. These brightly colored enlargements of the multiplication pictures from the Book For Kids are classroom size, (13" x 19"). Keep posted to reinforce the visual image. (15 per set)

FOR ADEQUATE EFFECTIVENESS

The *Times Tables The Fun Way* method is visually based. Please be sure that the students are shown the colored pictures found in the *Times Tables The Fun Way* Book For Kids or the *Times Tables The Fun Way* Posters while you are teaching the stories. This mental image is a crucial component of the picture-story method's effectiveness. Black and white reproductions are violations of the copyright and will impair success.

ADDITIONAL LEARNING ACTIVITIES

1. Ask students to make their own flashcards which illustrate the story. Make a new card each time a story is presented.

2. Ask students to make their own books. They can use their imagination to illustrate the stories. They should always include the fact and the answer that goes with the story. Each time a new story is presented, ask the students to illustrate it in their book.

3. Use the *Times Tables the Fun Way* Picture Flash Cards to ask students to repeat the story in their own words.

4. Sort the flash cards in sets of 10 or 12 and time students with each practice session. Students can try to beat their time on that particular group of cards. Cards are numbered with the lesson number on the bottom right corner.

HOW TO TEACH THE STORIES

1. Stimulate interest in the story by conducting a discussion. Each lesson contains lead questions to begin the discussions. When the story is finally introduced students will be more likely to remember the story because it will fit into something that they have discussed and experienced.

2. Tell the story to the students while they look at the picture in the text. This reinforces the story-number connection. Be as imaginative and creative as you can while telling the story. There is always room to add more details. Students love stories and will often be very attentive during this part of the learning process.

3. Ask a student to read the story out loud in the text. The rest of the class can read along.

4. Ask another student to read the caption at the end of the story.

5. Write the fact on the board and remind the students to look at the numbers of the fact and remember the story. Point out the similarities. For example: Don't these two eights look like snowmen? And remember how cold they are and that the sticks are for the fire. Sticks are for sounds like "64".

6. Ask the students to tell the story in their own words. (This is best done during the following lesson.)

7. Use additional learning activities as outlined above (i.e. students make own flashcards, and/ or book), and be sure to play plenty of games.

MATERIALS NECESSARY FOR TEACHING *TIMES TABLES THE FUN WAY*

1. *Times Tables The Fun Way* Book For Kids, (student text).

2. *Times Tables The Fun Way* Teacher's Manual

3. *Times Tables The Fun Way* Student Workbook. Master copies provided in Teacher's Manual or students may use the consumable workbooks available from Key Publishers.

4. *Times Tables The Fun Way* Flash Cards, (two sets), with pictures of number characters.

5. *Times Tables The Fun Way* Posters, (optional - but desirable).

6. Tokens, chips, or beans to issue points to winners of games.

7. Masking tape to draw lines on the rug for team starting point for various games.

8. Radio, tape player, or other noise making device for Musical Fives, lesson 4.

9. 4 or 5 small stuffed animals for Grab The Dinosaur Game, lesson 7.

10. Timer or clock.

11. Copies of game cards, grading templates, and awards from this manual pages 73 - 98. See individual lessons to determine the number of sets necessary.

12. Stamp to issue rewards in *Times Tables The Fun Way* Student Workbook Stamp and Score Sheet.

13. Chalkboard to play group games and teach lessons.

MASTER LESSON PLAN: OVERVIEW

Lesson 1	**Lesson 2**	**Lesson 3**	**Lesson 4**
Facts **Taught:** 3 x 3 4 x 3 1's & 2's 8 x 8 7 x 7	**Facts** **Taught:** 4 x 4 - 8 x 7 6 x 6 - 5's 6 x 4	**Facts** **Taught:** 6 x 3 6 x 8 9's	**Facts** **Taught:** 3 x 7 7 x 4
Pre-test	**Quiz:** #1	**Quiz:** #2	**Quiz:** #3
Timed Practice: 1's & 2's	**Timed Practice:** 5's	**Timed Practice:** 1's & 2's 9's	**Timed Practice:** 5's
Workbk. Pgs: 1-3	**Workbk. Pgs:** 4-14	**Workbk. Pgs:** 15-19	**Workbk. Pgs:** 20-26
Games:	**Games:** Name That Story: Game One Flash Card Relay Race: Game One	**Games:** Around the World	**Games:** Musical Fives Duck Duck Goose Story Tic Tac Toe

Lesson 5	**Lesson 6**	**Lesson 7**	**Lesson 8**
Facts **Taught:** 7 x 6 8 x 4	**Facts** **Taught:** 8 x 3	**Facts** **Reviewed**	**Facts** **Reviewed**
Quiz: #4	**Quiz:** #5	**Quiz:** #6	**Post-test**
Timed Practice: 9's	**Timed Practice:** 5's	**Timed Practice:** 9's	**Timed Practice:**
Workbk. Pgs: 27-32	**Workbk Pgs:** 33-39	**Workbk Pgs:** 40-42	**Workbk Pgs:**
Games: Name That Story: Game Two	**Games:** Pantomime Story Time Advancement	**Games:** Grab the Dinosaur Don't Say It	**Games:** Flash Card Relay Race: Game Two Crossword Puzzle

"TIMES TABLES THE FUN WAY"
Teacher's Manual

Section 1-1 *Getting Started*

Topic:
Students Fill Out Questionnaire

Goals:
To stimulate student interaction for later activities.
To show a personal interest in students.
To encourage students to be proud of their unique answers.
To let students know that *Times Tables the Fun Way* will be an exciting program.

Material:
TTTFW Workbook - Page 1

"TIMES TABLES THE FUN WAY"
WORKBOOK

STUDENT QUESTIONNAIRE

1. What is your full name? _____
2. Do you have a nickname? _____
3. What do you like best about school? _____
4. What is your favorite subject? _____
5. What is your favorite food? _____
6. Do you have a pet, if so, what kind? _____
7. If you could have one wish, any wish, what would it be? _____
8. What are your favorite things to do? _____
9. What do you want to be when you grow up? _____
10. Name one thing that you are very proud of: _____

Student Workbook Page 1

Activity:
Students fill out questionnaire and then exchange books and talk to their neighbor about their hobbies, wishes, etc. Teacher walks around the room and talks to individuals about their personal interests.

❖❖❖❖❖❖❖❖❖❖❖❖❖❖❖❖❖❖❖❖❖❖❖❖❖❖❖❖❖❖❖❖❖❖❖❖❖

Topic:
Introduce Method to Students

Goals:
Students will understand the importance of learning the times tables.

Explanation:
"Times tables are used in every grade from now on. You need to know your times tables to do multiplication, division, fractions, and decimals. So, it's really important to learn them well. You are very lucky because you will be learning in a way that is fun and easier than some other methods. I will be telling you some stories and you will be doing some worksheets and

"TIMES TABLES THE FUN WAY"
Teacher's Manual

Lesson 1

quizzes in your student workbook. We will also be playing games and you will receive rewards for doing well. Fifteen of the times tables facts will have stories that go with them. It will be very important that you learn these very well so that when you see a fact like 6 x 6, you will be able to remember the story and then the answer. Kids that learn by this method usually score higher on their final tests than with other methods. So, let's all have fun learning together."

Topic:
Give Pre-test...Time for 6 minutes

Goal:
The pre-test is used as an instrument to measure progress against the post-test.

Material:
TTTFW Workbook - Page 2

Explanation:
"Do as many of the facts as you can. Do not worry if you don't know the answers. The purpose of the test is to measure how much you will learn. At the end of the *Times Tables*

the Fun Way program, you will be given the same test again and that is when everyone will want to score 100%. Just do your best now. If you get done ahead of time just turn your paper over and sit quietly until time is up."

Answers:
TTTFW Teacher's Manual - Page 76: Grading Template

"TIMES TABLES THE FUN WAY"
WORKBOOK Lesson 1
PRE-TEST

correct: | % score:

48

NAME_____ DATE_____ TIME_____

2 x1	3 x2	4 x4	3 x6	7 x8	8 x9	1 x3	2 x4
5 x3	6 x4	8 x8	9 x4	1 x1	2 x2	5 x4	6 x6
9 x3	6 x9	7 x4	2 x9	4 x1	5 x2	5 x5	8 x6
9 x7	5 x7	9 x1	1 x5	0 x7	3 x7	6 x1	6 x7
8 x5	9 x9	3 x8	5 x9	4 x3	8 x1	7 x2	3 x0
7 x7	1 x7	2 x6	8 x4	5 x6	0 x9	3 x3	2 x8

Student Workbook Page 2

"TIMES TABLES THE FUN WAY"
Teacher's Manual

Topic:
Explain Reward System

Goals:
To motivate students to succeed while providing a summary of their progress.

Material:
TTTFW Workbook - Page 45

Explanation:
"Each student has a Stamp and Score Sheet. You will be keeping track of your scores and times on the practice sheets and quizzes. You can earn stamps for improving your time score

Student Workbook Page 45

and doing well on the quizzes and the practice sheets. We will have a class party when we have finished the workbook. Everyone that scores 100% on the post-test will receive a special award. " (Rewards can also be given at the end of lessons to students that cash in their stamps. See end of lesson 1 for details.)

❖◇❖

Topic:
Conduct Discussion On Times Tables

Goal:
To spark interest in times tables and to provide a preliminary understanding to facilitate further learning.

Discussion:
Start a discussion by asking: "Does anyone know what times tables are?" Possible answer: When you add up a lot of things you can use times tables to make adding easier. "Can anyone give an example of how you would use times tables in everyday life?" Possible Answer: If you went to the store to buy candy for 6 people and each piece was 5 cents, you could use times tables to figure out how much money you'll need. 6 people times 5 cents = 30 cents because 6 x 5 = 30. (Always compliment students on their answers to encourage discussion).

"TIMES TABLES THE FUN WAY"
Teacher's Manual

Topic:
Introduction To The Times Tables

Material:
TTTFW Student Text Pages 10 - 14

Activity:
Use tokens or chips to show 4 x 2 by making 4 piles with 2 in each pile and then 2 piles with four in each pile. Divide students in pairs and have them take turns showing their piles - (Use coins or other objects to make groups):

4 x 3

3 x 3

6 x 2

INTRODUCTION TO THE TIMES TABLES

Did you know that every time you go to the store you use times tables? If a piece of candy costs 5 cents and you have 7 friends you could add to figure out how much money you'll need. You could add 5 plus 5 plus 5 plus 5 plus 5 plus 5 plus 5. Or you could just figure it out in your head by using times tables. You would just ask yourself, "What is 5 cents times 7 friends?" 5 x 7 is 35 so you'll need 35 cents. It

Book for Kids Page 10

might sound like a lot of memorizing to learn all the times tables, but it's pretty easy if you just learn them one at a time. There are also some tricks in this book to help you along.

Times tables are really just a short-cut method of adding. They are often called multiplication facts. Times tables have two numbers that go together, such as 5 x 7 and an answer, such as 35. Or another example is 3 x 7 = 21. We'll show you how it works on the next page. We'll be using big, juicy, delicious apples.

Book for Kids Page 11

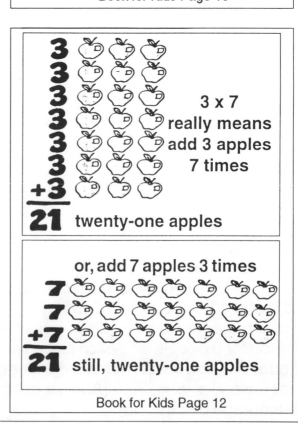

3 x 7 really means add 3 apples 7 times

twenty-one apples

or, add 7 apples 3 times

still, twenty-one apples

Book for Kids Page 12

"TIMES TABLES THE FUN WAY"
Teacher's Manual

Times tables are just an easy way to say, "add this number a certain number of times."
Let's try some more:

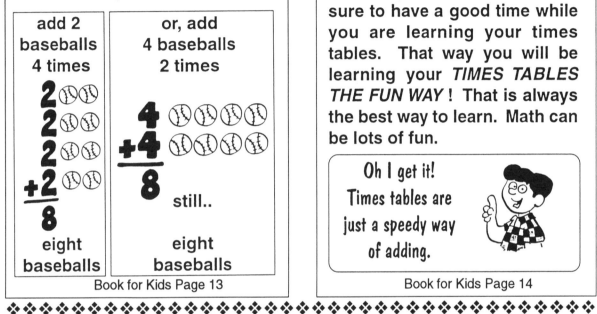

add 2 baseballs 4 times	or, add 4 baseballs 2 times

eight baseballs — eight baseballs

Book for Kids Page 13

So, now do you understand what times tables are? Or, maybe you already knew about times tables. The thing to remember is to be sure to have a good time while you are learning your times tables. That way you will be learning your *TIMES TABLES THE FUN WAY* ! That is always the best way to learn. Math can be lots of fun.

Oh I get it! Times tables are just a speedy way of adding.

Book for Kids Page 14

Topic:
Things You Should Know About Times Tables

Material:
TTTFW Student Text Pages 17 - 20

Activity:
Teacher reads page 17 and illustrates the commutative property on the blackboard.
Have students take turns reading pages 18 - 20
Use 2 dimes, quarter and a nickel to illustrate commutative property with coins in pockets.

When two numbers are multiplied, it doesn't matter which number is placed first. You will always get the same answer.

6		7
x7	and	x6
42		42

4		5
x5	and	x4
20		20

Book for Kids Page 17

"TIMES TABLES THE FUN WAY"
Teacher's Manual

Here is a little story to help you remember:

Let's say you have 50 cents to go to the store to buy candy.

You have: one quarter,
two dimes,
and one nickel.

If you put some of the coins in one pocket and the rest in the other pocket, it won't matter which coins are in which pocket. When you get to the store, and pull out your money you will still have 50 cents. This illustrates the commutative property of addition.

Book for Kids Page 18

50¢ here

50¢ here

The Commutative Property of Addition

Book for Kids Page 19

The commutative property is also true for multiplication. It simply means that when you multiply two or more numbers, the order in which they are written doesn't matter. You still get the same answer.

This is important to remember because this means that you only have to memorize half of your times tables.

Once you know that:	You also know that:
4 x2 8	2 x4 8

Book for Kids Page 20

Topic:
Teach The Ones

Material:
TTTFW Student Text Pages 22 - 24

Discussion:
Ask if anyone knows the answer to 99345 x 1.

Teacher's Notes:

One, two, three, four..
The number one is very important. When you start counting you always begin with one. If it wasn't for one, there probably wouldn't be any numbers at all.

Did you ever hear these sayings?
"one day at a time"
"we're number one"
"once in a lifetime"
"one step at a time"
"once and for all"

We use the number one for many things.

Book for Kids Page 22

One times any number is the same as saying, "add that number once."

One is like a mirror.

When five is with one, he looks back and sees himself so the answer is five.

$$\begin{array}{r} 5 \\ \underline{\times 1} \\ 5 \end{array}$$

Book for Kids Page 23

1	2	3
x1	x1	x1
1	2	3
4	5	6
x1	x1	x1
4	5	6
7	8	9
x1	x1	x1
7	8	9

$$\begin{array}{r} 2,465 \\ \underline{\times 1} \\ 2,465 \end{array} \qquad \begin{array}{r} 200,239 \\ \underline{\times 1} \\ 200,239 \end{array}$$

Ones are easy!
Book for Kids Page 24

❖ **Section 1-2**
❖ *Twos and Starting the Stories*
❖ **Topic:**
❖ The Twos
❖ **Goals:**
❖ To learn the twos by finger counting and then to memorize through repeated practice.
❖ **Material:** TTTFW St. Text Pg. 26 - 28
❖ **Activity:**
❖ Teach students to count by twos on their fingers. Start with the thumb and count 2, 4, 6, 8. The fourth finger is 8 so, 4 x 2 = 8. Quiz students orally on twos: Go around the room randomly asking what is 2 x 3, 6 x 2, 9 x 2, etc.

"TIMES TABLES THE FUN WAY"
Teacher's Manual

Lesson 1

Remember what "times" means. Two times a number means add that number twice. If you know how to add, the twos will be very easy.

2 x 5 is the same as 5 + 5.

5 + 5 = 10 so 2 x 5 = 10.

You can also count by twos on your fingers. Try 2 x 4. Count all the way to your 4th finger.

two, four, six, eight 4th finger

Oh, I get it! The answer is 8.

2 x 4 = 8

Book for Kids Page 26

Two times a number means add that number twice.

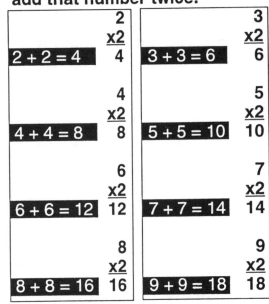

	2			3
	x2			x2
2 + 2 = 4	4		3 + 3 = 6	6
	4			5
	x2			x2
4 + 4 = 8	8		5 + 5 = 10	10
	6			7
	x2			x2
6 + 6 = 12	12		7 + 7 = 14	14
	8			9
	x2			x2
8 + 8 = 16	16		9 + 9 = 18	18

Twos are easy, too.

Book for Kids Page 27

Try these for extra practice:
What is 2 x 1?

2 x 5?

2 x 9?

2 x 3?

2 x 8?
Do you know all the answers?

You're getting smarter every minute.

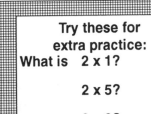

Book for Kids Page 28

❖ **Topic:**
❖ Teach Story 3 x 3
❖
❖ **Discussion:**
❖ Start a classroom discussion by
❖ asking the class a general question
❖ that pertains to the story line. For
❖ example, has anyone had triplets in
❖ their family or know anyone that has?
❖ Do you know the story of the three
❖ blind mice? After a few minutes of
❖ discussion, when interest is peaked,
❖ say, "Now I'm going to tell you a
❖ story about three very unique blind
❖ mice. Once upon a time....." (Teach-
❖ ers should elaborate on the story
❖ adding their own interpretation and

details.) After the story is told, ask a student to read the text out loud to the class. Then summarize the story by reminding the students that whenever they see 3 x 3, they should think of the three blind mice that were born with three tails each. That will remind them that the answer is 9, because there were 9 tails. Then write the fact on the board and point to the 3 x 3, saying, "Remember 3 x 3 is the story of the three blind baby mice." and point to the answer 9, saying, "remember they had 9 tails in all."

Material:
TTTFW Student Text Page 30

Section 1-3

Cheerleader Story and Ones and Twos Practice

Topic:
Teach Story 3 x 4

Discussion:
"Have you ever been to a basketball game? Why do they have cheerleaders? Do you want to be a cheerleader?"

Material:
TTTFW Student Text Page 31

3 x 3 = 9

Out in the country lived a blind mama mouse. She was very happy because she just found out that she would be having triplets. She was worried about one thing. She had a cousin that was born without a tail. Every time the cousin tried to sit up, he would fall over because he had no tail to keep his balance. The mama mouse hoped and hoped that her babies would each have a tail. The birthday came and to the mama's delight, each baby had not one tail....but three tails each. The mama mouse was so proud.

Book for Kids Page 30

3 x 4 = 12

There is a cheer that kids say to help them remember that 3 x 4 = 12. It's very easy and it is a lot of fun. It goes like this:

I LIKE MATH! LET'S DO SOME MORE!

One...Two...Three...Four....I like math let's do some more. 4 *four* (I like math, let's do some more!)

$$\begin{array}{r} 4 \textit{ four} \\ \underline{\times 3} \textit{ three} \\ 1\,2 \textit{ one...two} \end{array}$$

Book for Kids Page 31

"TIMES TABLES THE FUN WAY"
Teacher's Manual

Lesson 1

Activity:
Follow the format outlined in the 3 x 3 story to teach this as well as all of the following stories. You can also refer to the description of how to teach the stories on page iv in the introduction of this manual.

❖❖❖

Topic:
Review Stories 3 x 4, 3 x 3, Twos

Discussion:
Ask students to recite the story for 4 x 3 and then 3 x 3. Call on students at random to give answers to the following: 2 x 2, 3 x 2, 5 x 2, 8 x 2, 9 x 2, 4 x 2. If they stumble, count out loud with students demonstrating with finger counting.

❖❖❖

Topic:
Ones and Twos Timed Practice Sheet

Goals:
To finish the sheet as fast as possible and still score 100%

Material:
TTTFW Workbook Page 3

Explanation:
"Try to fill in the answers as quickly as you can while taking care to be accurate. You will get a stamp for scoring 100%, but you also can get a stamp for improving your own score. The object is to do it faster next time to show that you are improving. It doesn't matter what time your neighbor gets because you are competing with yourself, not your neighbor. When you are done with the practice sheet, look at the clock and write your time down on the paper. I will write on the board when 1 minute has elapsed, 2 minutes, 3 minutes, etc. You write the minute and the seconds

| "TIMES TABLES THE FUN WAY" WORKBOOK Lesson 1 ONES AND TWOS TIMED PRACTICE | # correct: | % score: 20 |

NAME_____ DATE_____ TIME_____

1 x 1	1 x 2	3 x 1	6 x 1
8 x 1	9 x 1	7 x 1	5 x 1
1 x 4	2 x 2	5 x 2	2 x 6
2 x 9	8 x 2	7 x 2	2 x 4
2 x 3	3 x 3	4 x 3	497 x 1

Student Workbook Page 3

on your paper like this: 2:53. Be sure to put your time in the box marked time. When you are done with your sheet, just turn your workbook over and sit quietly. Do you have any questions? Is everyone ready? On your mark, get set GO." (Teacher puts a 1 on board when 1 minute has elapsed. At two minutes, teacher erases the 1 and puts a 2. Students will note their own seconds).

❖❖❖

Topic:
Grading The Ones and Twos Timed Practice Sheet

Material:
TTTFW Workbook Page 3

Activity:
"Everyone exchange workbooks with your neighbor. I will read the answers and you should put an x through the answer if it is incorrect or if it is blank. (Teacher reads row 1 across, row 2 across, etc.) Ok now put your neighbor's score, # correct, at the top of the page and then give the workbooks back to their owners. Now you can put your own score on your Stamp and Score Sheet, (page 45 of the workbook). At the end of the lesson, you can bring your workbooks to me and I will stamp your score sheet and issue rewards." Instead of class grading, teacher may use templates to grade the Timed Practice Sheets.

Answers: TTTFW Teacher's Manual - Page 73: Grading Template

❖❖❖

Section 1- 4   ***Snowman and Soldier Stories***
Topic:
Teach Story 8 x 8

Discussion: "Have you ever been camping during the winter? What kind of snow makes the best snowman; dry and light, or heavy and wet?"

Material:
TTTFW Student Text Pages 68 - 69

"TIMES TABLES THE FUN WAY"
Teacher's Manual

8 x 8 = 64

It was the middle of winter and very cold. The forest was quiet because all the animals were asleep for the winter.

Two snowmen decided to go camping. By the time they arrived, they were very cold. They found a pile a sticks. The sign said it was OK to use the sticks for the fire.

They built a nice fire with the wood. The only trouble was that when they got close to the fire they started to shrink. Do you know why?

Book for Kids Page 68

Remember: When 8 is with 8, they are two snowmen who are very cold and the sticks (6) are for (4) the fire.

Book for Kids Page 69

Topic:
Teach Story 7 x 7

Discussion:
"What would happen if everyone threw their trash out of their car windows? What's wrong with trash along the highways?" ....ugly, unclean, doesn't decompose.

Material:
TTTFW Student Text Pages 58 - 59

Teacher's Notes: _____
_____
_____

7 x 7 = 49

7 and 7 are soldiers in charge of litter control. On weekends they go to Look-Out Hill and sit inside the little hole. They watch day and night to be sure that no one throws litter out of their windows. The 7 soldiers love to see the countryside clean and full of new flowers. The purpose of their job is to keep America beautiful.

They put the flag on the hill to remind people that America is a place to be proud of and it's everyone's duty to keep it clean.

Look out, the 7's will be watching you!

Book for Kids Page 58

"TIMES TABLES THE FUN WAY"
Teacher's Manual

Remember: When 7 is with 7, they are soldiers who sit in their hole (4) and make sure that they keep America (9) clean.

Book for Kids Page 59

❖ **Topic:**
❖ Review 3 x 3, 3 x 4, 8 x 8, & 7 x 7

❖ **Discussion:** Ask volunteers to tell the above stories in their own words. Tell Students: We've already learned 21 facts!!!

Teacher's Notes:
_____
_____
_____
_____
_____
_____
_____

Topic:
Issue Stamps

Material: TTTFW Workbook - Page-45

Activity:
Ask students to bring workbooks up to the teacher so stamps can be issued. When a student has accumulated 10 stamps, they can be given a coupon. Two coupons can be used as a Homework Pass, (no homework due for one assignment of the student's choice or other rewards as determined by the teacher.)

Awards:
TTTFW Teacher's Manual - Page 98

"TIMES TABLES THE FUN WAY"
STAMP AND SCORE SUMMARY SHEET

Lesson 1	Lesson 2	Lesson 3	Lesson 4
Pre-test Score: _____ Time: _____	Quiz # 1 Facts: ____ Stories: ____	Quiz # 2 Facts: ____ Stories: ____	Quiz # 3 Facts: ____ Stories: ____
1's & 2's Practice Score: _____ Time: _____	Fives Practice Score: _____ Time: _____	1's & 2's Practice Score: _____ Time: _____	Fives Practice Score: _____ Time: _____
		Nines Practice Score: _____ Time: _____	
Stamps:	Stamps:	Stamps:	Stamps:

Lesson 5	Lesson 6	Lesson 7	Lesson 8
Quiz # 4 Facts: ____ Stories: ____	Quiz # 5 Facts: ____ Stories: ____	Quiz # 7 Facts: ____ Stories: ____	Post-test Score: _____ Time: _____
Nines Practice Score: _____ Time: _____	Fives Practice Score: _____ Time: _____	Homework Quiz: Score: _____	
Story Quiz Facts: ____ Stories: ____		Nines Practice Score: _____ Time: _____	
Stamps:	Stamps:	Stamps:	Stamps:

Student Workbook Page 45

"TIMES TABLES THE FUN WAY"
Teacher's Manual

Lesson 2

Section 2 - 1 *Quiz and Hang Glider Story*

Topic:
Quiz # 1...give 5 minutes to complete

Goals:
Students will remember stories that go with the facts so that they can illustrate them. Give clues if necessary.

Material:
TTTFW Workbook - Page 4

Explanation:
"You will have five minutes to complete the quiz. You will not be recording your time so you don't have to try to hurry. Just try to finish it in five minutes."

Answers:
TTTFW Teacher's Manual - Page 69:
Teachers should grade the quizzes to assess progress and enjoy the student's story - art work.

❖◆❖◆❖◆❖◆❖◆❖◆❖◆❖◆❖◆❖◆❖◆❖◆❖◆❖◆❖◆❖◆❖◆❖◆❖

Topic:
Teach Story 4 x 4

Discussion:
"What happens when you turn 16? Do you know anyone that flies hang gliders? Have you ever seen anyone fly a hang glider?"

Material:
TTTFW Student Text Page 34 - 35

"TIMES TABLES THE FUN WAY"
WORKBOOK Lesson 2

QUIZ # 1 NAME_____ DATE_____

Answer these facts:

3	7	3	8
x 3	x 7	x 4	x 8

CORRECT
4

What is the story for 8 x 8 ?
Draw it or write it.

What is the story for 3 x 3 ?
Draw it or write it.

CORRECT

CORRECT

What is the story for 7 x 7 ?
Draw it or write it.

What is the story for 3 x 4 ?
Draw it or write it.

CORRECT

CORRECT

Student Workbook Page 4

Teacher's Notes:

_____
_____
_____
_____
_____
_____
_____
_____
_____

4 x 4 = 16

Bart loved hang gliding. He learned to fly when he was 14. The only thing that he didn't like was hiking his hang glider to the top of the hill so he could fly down. He wished he was 16 so he could drive and that he had a four wheel drive to get to the top of the hill. He went to Bernie's Burgers and got a job working after school. By the time he turned 16 he saved enough money to buy a 4 by 4. He was so happy because his trip up the hill was almost as much fun as flying down.

Book for Kids Page 34

Remember: When 4 is with 4, the fours become a 4 by 4 (4 x 4) and you have to be 16 to drive it.

Book for Kids Page 35

Section 2 - 2
Magic Pond Story and Review

Topic:
Teach Story 6 x 4

Discussion:
"If you could be any animal you wanted, what would it be and why? Would you rather be a snail or a swan? Would you rather fly or swim? Why?"

Material:
TTTFW Student Text Pages 44 - 45

6 x 4 = 24

There was once a snail that lived in a swamp with lily-pads. The swamp was pretty ordinary, but next to it was a special magic four pond.

The snail knew that if he climbed into the magic pond he would have one wish granted. The snail had become tired of always looking at the ground. He wished he could soar above the trees and mountains like a swan. So, he climbed up into the magic pond.

The snail closed his eyes very tightly and made his wish. Poof! His wish came true and he turned into a beautiful swan.

Book for Kids Page 44

"TIMES TABLES THE FUN WAY"
Teacher's Manual

Lesson 2

Remember: When 6 is with 4, 6 is a snail in a magic pond (4). The snail gets his wish to become a swan (2), thanks to the magic pond (4).

Book for Kids Page 45

Topic:
Review Stories 8 x 8, 7 x 7, 6 x 4, 4 x 4, 3 x 4, 3 x 3

Goals:
Students will be able to remember which stories go with which facts.

Activity:
Ask students to recite the stories in their own words. Always welcome variations and elaboration.

Teacher's Notes:
_____
_____
_____

Section 2 - 3 *Bouncy Guy and Thirsty Sixes Stories*

Topic:
Teach Story 8 x 7

Discussion:
"Do you ever get bored watching TV? Would you rather have a trampoline or a swimming pool in your back yard?" AFTER THE STORY: "Why do you think 7 is a bouncy guy?" ANSWER: "He only has one leg. He can't walk. He has to hop and bounce."

Material:
TTTFW Student Text - Page 66 - 67

7 x 8 = 56
7 is a bouncy sort of guy. He loves to play, and he loves to hop. In fact, he set up a playground in his back yard.

When 7 finishes his homework and he grows tired of watching TV, he hops out his back door to have some fun.

First 7 bounces on one side of his trampoline. Then he bounces on the other side of the tramp. This time 7 bounces very high, right over to his diving board. On hot days he dives right into the pool. What a nice cool relief!

Book for Kids Page 66

Remember: When 7 is with 8, 7 bounces on his trampoline (8) over to the diving board (5) and into the pool (6).

Book for Kids Page 67

❖ **Topic:**
Teach Story 6 x 6

❖ **Discussion:**
"Have you ever been to the desert? What is it like? Why is it so dry there? What is an oasis?"

❖ **Material:**
TTTFW Student Text Page 46 - 47

Teacher's Notes:
_____
_____
_____
_____
_____

6 x 6 = 36

There were twin sixes from Africa. They wanted to visit their cousins who lived across the desert. They hadn't seen each other for many years.

They set out on their journey. After hiking for many days they got low on water. Just when they started to get very worried, they came upon a pool of clear, cool, spring water.

The twin sixes were so happy to find water. They were very thirsty sixes. After getting a drink they made it to their cousin's house where they had a glorious party.

Book for Kids Page 46

Remember: When 6 is with 6 they are very thirsty sixes (36).

Book for Kids Page 47

"TIMES TABLES THE FUN WAY"
Teacher's Manual

Lesson 2

Section 2 - 4 *Learning The Fives and Name That Story Game*
Topic:
Teach The Fives

Material: TTTFW Student Text Pages 38 - 40

Explanation:
Explain pages 39 and 40 of the student text. Demonstrate counting by fives on your fingers.

Activity:
Go around the room counting by fives, first student says "5", next student says "10" , etc. When student says "50", the next person should start over with 5. After two rounds make a sound like: beep beep. When the beep sounds, that student has to say what number times 5 equals the answer they just said....Example: 5, 10, 15, 20, 25, 30...beep beep. What number times 5 equals 30? The answer is 6 because 6 x 5 = 30. Class continues counting by fives until the beep sounds again.

Remember the finger counting trick you learned for the twos? The same trick will work with the fives. All you have to learn is how to count by fives. Do you already know how?

Book for Kids Page 38

If you can count by fives, you already know your fives!

Let's try it.

Book for Kids Page 39

"TIMES TABLES THE FUN WAY"
Teacher's Manual

1 x5 5	2 x5 10	3 x5 15
4 x5 20	5 x5 25	6 x5 30
7 x5 35	8 x5 40	9 x5 45

Soon you will get so good at finding the answer, you will just remember your fives without counting on your fingers. Keep practicing.

Book for Kids Page 40

❖ **Topic:**
❖ Fives Timed Practice Sheet

❖ **Goal:**
❖ To finish the sheet as fast as possible and still score 100%

❖ **Material:**
❖ TTTFW Student Workbook-Page 5

❖ **Explanation:**
"Try to fill in the answers as quickly as you can while taking care to be accurate. You will get a stamp for scoring 100%, but you can also get a stamp for improving your own score. The object is to do it faster next time to show that you are improving. It doesn't matter what

time your neighbor gets because you are competing with yourself, not your neighbor. When you are done with the practice sheet, look at the clock and write your time down on the paper. I will write on the board when 1 minute has elapsed, 2 minutes, 3 minutes, etc. You write the minute and the seconds on your paper like this - 2:53. Be sure to put your time in the box marked time. When you are done with your sheet, just turn your workbook over and sit quietly. Do you have any questions? You may begin."

Teacher's Notes:
_____
_____
_____

"TIMES TABLES THE FUN WAY"
WORKBOOK Lesson 2
FIVES TIMED PRACTICE

# correct:	% score:
	20

NAME_____ DATE_____ TIME_____

1 x 5	5 x 5	9 x 5	5 x 4
6 x 5	4 x 5	8 x 5	5 x 3
7 x 5	3 x 5	5 x 2	5 x 8
5 x 1	5 x 9	5 x 6	5 x 7
3 x 3	4 x 3	8 x 8	7 x 7

Student Workbook Page 5

Lesson 2

Topic:
Grading The Fives Practice Sheet

Material:
TTTFW Workbook - Page 5

Explanation:
"Everyone exchange workbooks with your neighbor. I will read the answers and you should put an- x through the answer if it is incorrect or if it is blank. (Teacher reads row 1 across, row 2 across, etc.) Ok now put your neighbor's score at the top of the page and then give the workbooks back to their owner. Now you can put your own score on your Stamp and Score Sheet (page 45 of the workbook). At the end of the lesson, you can bring your workbooks to me and I will stamp your score sheet and issue rewards." Instead of class grading, teacher may use templates to grade the Timed Practice Sheets.

Answers:
TTTFW Teachers Manual - Page 74: Grading Template

❖❖❖❖❖❖❖❖❖❖❖❖❖❖❖❖❖❖❖❖❖❖❖❖❖❖❖❖❖❖❖❖❖

Topic:
Game: Name That Story: Game One

Goal:
To reinforce the story number connection in an exciting game format.

Material:
TTTFW Teacher's Manual
Page 78-79: Name that Story Game One Cards - one set for each group. Make copies on cardstock, if necessary, and cut cards apart.

Activity:
Show the cards to the class one by one. The first person to say both the story that goes along with the fact and the whole fact with the answer wins. Give a point to that person. The students with the top points will be the team captains. Now divide into groups of 2-5 kids. The team captain shows a card

to the first two students. They race to say the answer. The first one to say the story and the whole fact gets a point. (Chips or tokens can be given to keep track of points). The captain then shows the next card to the next two students. Continue around the circle until all the cards have been used 2 times. The student with the most points is the winner.

Example: Card is 7 x 7, student says, "there are two soldiers on litter patrol so 7 x 7 = 49." Students must say the whole fact and at least one word from the story to show they know it. Captains should switch positions of students so that the winners sit next to each other and must compete amongst themselves, this gives every one a chance for a point. At the end of the session, students who won their group session should get a stamp on their score sheet, and captains should also receive a stamp in the box marked: "Won Game".

❖❖❖❖❖❖❖❖❖❖❖❖❖❖❖❖❖❖❖❖❖❖❖❖❖❖❖❖❖❖❖❖❖❖❖❖❖❖

Section 2 - 5   *Double Digits - Double The Fun*
Topic:
Teach Double Digit By One Digit Multiplication

Explanation:
Put this problem on the board: 25 x 5. "Does anyone know the answer? Let me put it this way, if you had 5 quarters, (25 cents each), how much money would you have? Right. $1.25. Or to figure it out you could go like this: Write on board in a column 25 + 25 + 25 + 25 + 25 = . Add the columns showing the addition and write the answer 125 or $1.25 if you're talking about money. "I'm going to show you a very fast and easy short-cut. But first I want to tell you a little story: Double digit multiplication is like being in the army. You have to stay in formation or the troops get out of line. Soldiers march in a perfectly straight line and the general goes down the row making sure that one foot isn't out of line in his perfect row of soldiers. Well, that's what you have to do with double digit multiplication...keep your numbers perfectly lined up.

OK, now I'm going to show you how to do it." Put 23 x 2 on the board. Show how you multiply 3 x 2 then 2 x 2, circle the numbers you are multiplying. Explain how to keep the numbers lined up by drawing column lines on the board.   Show how to do 42 x 3 on the board.

❖❖❖❖❖❖❖❖❖❖❖❖❖❖❖❖❖❖❖❖❖❖❖❖❖❖❖❖❖❖❖❖❖❖❖❖❖❖

Lesson 2

Topic:
Learning Double Digit Multiplication

Material:
TTTFW Workbook - Pages 6 and 7

Activity:
Students practice newly learned skill by reading and filling in the wbk. pages.

"TIMES TABLES THE FUN WAY"
WORKBOOK Lesson 2
LEARNING DOUBLE DIGIT MULTIPLICATION

Let's do one together, and then you'll be able to do it yourself.

First, ask yourself what is 4 x 2?
$$\begin{array}{r} 5\,4 \\ \times\,2 \\ \hline ? \end{array}$$

Right! the answer is 8.
So, put the 8 right under the 2.
$$\begin{array}{r} 5\,4 \\ \times\,2 \\ \hline 8 \end{array}$$

Now ask yourself, what is 5 x 2?
$$\begin{array}{r} 5\,4 \\ \times\,2 \\ \hline ? \end{array}$$

Right, the answer is 10, so put the 10 with it's 0 right under the 5.
$$\begin{array}{r} 5\,4 \\ \times\,2 \\ \hline 1\,0\,8 \end{array}$$

The most important thing to learn is to keep your numbers lined up in very neat columns. This is important because it will help you get the right answer when you learn to do problems like:
$$\begin{array}{r} 5\,4 \\ \times\,5\,4 \end{array}$$

Go on to the next page

Student Workbook Page 6

"TIMES TABLES THE FUN WAY"
WORKBOOK Lesson 2
LEARNING DOUBLE DIGIT *Page Two*

Now try this one yourself:

Ask yourself what is 2 x 3? Put your answer in the box:
$$\begin{array}{r} 6\,3 \\ \times\,2 \end{array}$$

Now ask yourself what is 6 x 2? Put your answer in the boxes to the left of your 6:
$$\begin{array}{r} 6\,3 \\ \times\,2 \\ \hline 6 \end{array}$$

Good Job! Now try these:

$$\begin{array}{r} 3\,5 \\ \times\,1 \end{array} \qquad \begin{array}{r} 2\,3 \\ \times\,2 \end{array} \qquad \begin{array}{r} 4\,2 \\ \times\,3 \end{array} \qquad \begin{array}{r} 3\,4 \\ \times\,2 \end{array} \qquad \begin{array}{r} 2\,4 \\ \times\,2 \end{array}$$

You're doing great! Can you do these? Be sure to keep your columns straight.

$$\begin{array}{r} 29 \\ \times1 \end{array} \qquad \begin{array}{r} 31 \\ \times3 \end{array} \qquad \begin{array}{r} 32 \\ \times3 \end{array} \qquad \begin{array}{r} 41 \\ \times4 \end{array} \qquad \begin{array}{r} 43 \\ \times2 \end{array}$$

Student Workbook Page 7

Section 2 - 6   *Double Digit And Carrying To The Neighbor*

Topic:
Teach Double Digit By One Digit With Carrying

Goals:
Students will be able to multiply and add in the same problem while keeping numbers in straight columns.

Explanation:
Put 25 x 5 on the board: "What is 5 x 5? Right, it's 25. Now put the 5 right under the 5 and carry the two to the neighbor. (Put the two in its waiting place, the square above the 2.)

"TIMES TABLES THE FUN WAY"
WORKBOOK Lesson 2
LEARNING DOUBLE DIGIT MULTIPLICATION
WITH CARRYING

Let's do one together, and then you'll be able to do it yourself.

First, ask yourself what is 4 x 3?
$$\begin{array}{r} 5\,4 \\ \times\,3 \\ \hline ? \end{array}$$

Right! The answer is 12.
But there is only one column for the 12, so you have to squeeze the 1 into its waiting place......
$$\begin{array}{r} 1 \\ 5\,4 \\ \times\,3 \\ \hline 2 \end{array}$$

Now ask yourself, what is 5 x 3?
$$\begin{array}{r} 5\,4 \\ \times\,3 \\ \hline ? \end{array}$$

Right, the answer is 15, but before you write it you have to add the number in the waiting place, so ask yourself what is 15 + 1 ?

Right, 15 + 1 is 16. Now you can write the answer in its column.
$$\begin{array}{r} 5\,4 \\ \times\,3 \\ \hline 1\,6\,2 \end{array}$$
Go on to the next page

Student Workbook Page 8

Now what is 2 x 5? Right, it's 10. Now add the number in the waiting place to it ....10 + 2 = 12. Put the twelve in a neat row to the left of the 5. That's your answer, 125. That's a lot easier than adding up 25 + 25 + 25 + 25 + 25 isn't it?"

"TIMES TABLES THE FUN WAY"
Teacher's Manual

Material:
TTTFW Workbook - Pages 8, 9, and 10

Activity:
Students do worksheets while teacher walks around room giving individual help. After the students have finished page 10, they should cor-

---

"TIMES TABLES THE FUN WAY"
WORKBOOK Lesson 2
DOUBLE DIGIT WITH CARRYING Page Two

Now try this one:

Ask yourself what is 4 x 3? Write your answer:

6 3
x 4

Now ask yourself what is 6 x 4?

6 3
x 4
?

Ok, now keep the answer to 6 x 4 in your mind while you add the number from the waiting place.

Now write your answer.

6 3
x 4

Good Job ! Now try these:

2 5   3 6   2 8   2 2   5 3
x 2   x 2   x 2   x 7   x 4

On on to the next page

Student Workbook Page 9

"TIMES TABLES THE FUN WAY"
WORKBOOK Lesson 2

DOUBLE DIGIT WITH CARRYING Page Three

Excellent! Now try these: Be sure to keep your columns straight.

6 2	8 2	1 8	2 7	5 5
x 6	x 8	x 7	x 7	x 5

Now check your answers by turning to the back of the book. Then put your number correct here:

 # correct

22

Let's try doing some real easy stuff. Did you remember that zero times any number is always zero, because zero is the chief?

See if you can do these:

0	7	0	9	6	0	4	5	8	95
x1	x0	x8	x0	x0	x3	x0	x0	x0	x0

Wow! That was easy!

Student Workbook Page 10

---

rect their own pages and put the number correct in the box on page 10. The answers appear on the last page of the workbook.

❖❖❖❖❖❖❖❖❖❖❖❖❖❖❖❖❖❖❖❖❖❖❖❖❖❖❖❖❖❖❖❖❖❖❖❖

Section 2 - 7
Zero Is The Chief And Game Time

Topic:
Teach The Zeroes

Material:
TTTFW Student Text - Page 16

Explanation:
"Zero times any number is always zero. Whenever you have to multiply a number times zero, it's like you don't even have to think. You get a little break. Just put zero for your answer. 7 x 0 = 0 and 234,667 x 0 = 0. Now that you know

---

THINGS YOU SHOULD KNOW ABOUT TIMES TABLES

The first and easiest thing to remember is that zero times any number is zero. That's because zero is the "chief". When any number is with zero, the chief takes over and the answer is always zero.

Let's try some:
What is 0 x 5?
Right! It's 0.

What is 0 x 3?
0 x 9 ?
0 x 10 ?
0 x 936 ?

Zero: "THE CHIEF"

They all have the same answer because the chief took over. It's zero.
Book for Kids Page 16

"TIMES TABLES THE FUN WAY"
Teacher's Manual

double digit multiplication and the zero rule, you can figure out your tens, elevens, and twelves, and you won't have to memorize them."

Material:
TTTFW Workbook - Pages 11, 12, 13, and 14

Answers:
TTTFW Teacher's Manual - Page 69

❖❖❖❖❖❖❖❖

Topic:
Relay Race: Game One

Goal: Try to be the first team to complete the stack of 32 cards.

"TIMES TABLES THE FUN WAY"
WORKBOOK Lesson 2
TENS ELEVENS AND TWELVES

REMEMBER THAT ZERO TIMES ANY NUMBER IS ZERO.

11	10	12	10	11	12	10
x2	x3	x3	x2	x1	x2	x5

12	10	12	11	11	10	12
x5	x7	x6	x7	x9	x9	x4

12	10	11	10	11	12	10
x1	x8	x8	x1	x6	x9	x4

12	11	11	10	11	10	12
x8	x3	x4	x6	x5	x5	x2

Congratulations! Now you know how to figure out the tens, elevens, and twelves.

Go on to the next page

Student Workbook Page 11

"TIMES TABLES THE FUN WAY"
WORKBOOK Lesson 2
WORKSHEET # 1

12	11	14	33	17
x3	x4	x3	x3	x7

18	17	22	33	32
x8	x2	x7	x4	x3

36	24	11	12	22
x2	x3	x9	x9	x8

27	28	12	12	12
x7	x8	x7	x5	x4

Student Workbook Page 12

"TIMES TABLES THE FUN WAY"
WORKBOOK Lesson 2
WORKSHEET # 1a

25	45	43	52	57
x3	x4	x3	x3	x7

28	47	22	32	55
x8	x2	x5	x4	x3

78	44	21	66	77
x2	x3	x9	x6	x8

28	27	72	52	32
x7	x8	x7	x5	x4

Student Workbook Page 13

"TIMES TABLES THE FUN WAY"
WORKBOOK Lesson 2
WORKSHEET # 1b

52	44	26	52	27
x3	x5	x6	x5	x7

18	58	66	32	35
x8	x2	x5	x2	x5

65	33	23	61	88
x2	x4	x3	x6	x7

77	28	82	72	32
x7	x8	x7	x5	x3

Student Workbook Page 14

---

complete the stack of 32 cards.

Set-up: Sort two sets of *Times Tables The Fun Way* Flash Cards so that only the cards from lesson 1 and 2 are included. This should represent 32 of the facts that have been covered so far. Peel off two strips of masking tape and put them on the rug, an equal distance from the team heads. Select two team captains to flash the cards to their respective teams.

Activity:

How to Play: (See diagram)
John comes to captain 1 and looks at the first card. John says the answer to the captain. If he is correct, he turns to the class and says the whole fact and the answer. He then runs back to the first person in his line, Sue, and tags her. John then goes to the back of the line and Sue comes up to the captain and answers the second card in the captain's pile. Play continues until all the cards have been answered.

If a student doesn't know the answer in 5 seconds, they should tag the next person and go to the end of the line. The tagged person must try to answer the card that was previously missed.

Captain with flash cards — Team 1 — Masking Tape — John, Sue, Mary — Single File Line

Captain with flash cards — Team 2 — Masking Tape — Bob, Tom, Sally — Single File Line

The two teams play simultaneously, racing to complete the 32 card pile. All members of the winning team should receive a stamp on the Stamp and Score Sheet in the box marked: won game.

Topic:

Issue Stamps

Material: TTTFW Workbook - Page 45: Stamp and Score Sheet

Activity: Ask students to bring workbooks up to the teacher so stamps can be issued. When a student has accumulated 10 stamps, they can be given a coupon. Two coupons can be used as a Homework Pass (no homework due for one assignment of the student's choice or other rewards as determined by the teacher).

Awards: TTTFW Teacher's Manual Page 98: Make copies and cut apart

"TIMES TABLES THE FUN WAY"
Teacher's Manual

Section 3 - 1   *Quiz and The Big Foot Story*

Topic:
Quiz #2...give 5 minutes to complete

Goals:
Students will remember stories that go with the facts so that they can illustrate them. Give clues if necessary.

Explanation:
"You will have five minutes to complete the quiz. You will not be recording your time so you don't have to try to hurry. Just try to finish it in five minutes."

Material:
TTTFW Workbook - Page 15

Answers:
TTTFW Teacher's Manual - Page 69, teacher grades

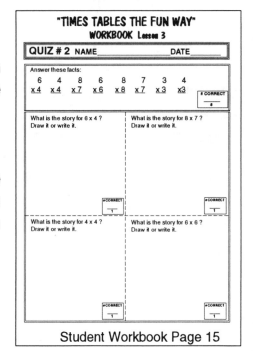

Student Workbook Page 15

Topic:
Review Stories and Facts

Goal:
Students will be able to remember which stories go with which facts.

Activity:
Ask students to recite the stories in their own words. Always welcome variations and elaboration.

Stories covered so far:

    8 x 8 Snowmen
    6 x 6 Thirsty Sixes
    7 x 7 Soldiers
    8 x 7 Bouncy Guy
    6 x 4 Magic Pond
    4 x 4 Hang Glider
    3 x 4 Cheer
    3 x 3 Three Mice

"TIMES TABLES THE FUN WAY"
Teacher's Manual

Topic:
Ones and Twos Timed Practice Sheet

Goal:
To finish the sheet as fast as possible and still score 100%

Explanation:
"OK, now we are going to do the Ones and Twos Timed Practice Sheet again. Be sure to go as fast as you can and try to beat your last time and score on the Ones and Twos Sheet. When you are done, write down your time and work on any of your unfinished workbook pages but don't work ahead of page 16. Everyone ready? Ok, Go."

Material:
TTTFW Workbook - Page 16

"TIMES TABLES THE FUN WAY" WORKBOOK Lesson 3 ONES AND TWOS TIMED PRACTICE	# correct:	% score: 20

NAME_____ DATE____ TIME____

1 x 1	1 x 2	3 x 1	6 x 1
8 x 1	9 x 1	7 x 1	5 x 1
1 x 4	2 x 2	5 x 2	2 x 6
2 x 9	8 x 2	7 x 2	2 x 4
2 x 3	3 x 3	4 x 3	497 x 1

Student Workbook Page 16

Topic:
Grading The Ones and Twos Practice Sheet

Material:
TTTFW Workbook - Page 16

Activity:
Class exchanges books and fills out Stamp / Score Sheet

Answers:
TTTFW Teacher's Manual - Page 73: Grading Template

Teacher's Notes:

Lesson 3

Topic: Teach Story 6 x 3

Discussion: "Has anyone heard of Big Foot? Do you think he exists?"

Material: TTTFW Student Text Page 42 - 43

6 x 3 = 18

6 loves to go out target shooting on weekends. One particular Saturday when 6 was in the forest practicing with her bow and arrow, she spotted a very large hairy creature with great big feet. 6 wondered if he was the legendary Big Foot.

6 didn't want to hurt the creature, but she wanted to stop him from coming any closer. So, she shot her arrow straight up into the air. It landed right in front of the hairy creature, stopping him dead in his tracks.

Book for Kids Page 42

Remember: When 6 is with 3, 6 shoots her bow (3). The arrow (1) lands in front of Big Foot (8).

Book for Kids Page 43

Section 3 - 2   *Birthday Cake Story and The Nines*

Topic:
Teach Story 6 x 8

Discussion:

"What would it be like if you never had a birthday celebration? Do you think you would be very happy for just a small gift if you had never received one before?"

Material: TTTFW Student Text Page 48 - 49

"TIMES TABLES THE FUN WAY"
Teacher's Manual

6 x 8 = 48

There once lived a king and queen in a castle. A wicked witch put a spell on the place so that no one could have a child. The king travelled to Magic Land and spoke to the fairy. She said she could break the spell but, "your child will be born in the shape of an eight. Her birthday must be kept secret for 8 years." The king said OK and left. Sure enough they had a baby 8. The child never had a birthday party until the day she turned eight. She was sitting in the kitchen and the chef arrived. He announced, "The cake is for the 8," and the spell was broken.

Book for Kids Page 48

Remember: When 6 is with 8, 6 is the chef and the cake is in the shape of an 8. The cake is "for the eight." (48)

Book for Kids Page 49

Topic:
Teach The Nines: Adding Method

Goals:
Students will learn to figure out the answers to the nines using the adding method.

Material:
TTTFW Student Text Pages 72 - 78

Discussion:
Read pages 72 and 73 then, "turn to page 74 in your textbook. Fold the book over so that only page 74 is showing. Look very closely at the facts and the

Book for Kids Page 72

"TIMES TABLES THE FUN WAY"
Teacher's Manual

answers. What can you notice about the nines?" Call on students and compliment them on their answers. Anything that they notice is correct.

After everyone has had a chance giving their answers..."Turn your book over and look at page 75. Do you see that the answer always starts with one less than the number that nine is multiplied by?" Take a few minutes to explain. Then give random nine facts and ask students to say what number is one less, i.e. 9 x 5......4, 9 x 6.....5 "Now what if I said 6 x 9? Would one less be 8 or would it be 5? Here is a hint: Always use the number that nine is multiplied by. Never use 9 to figure out one less (unless of course its 9 x 9)."

When students understand, turn to page 76. "It says, if you add up the digits in the answer, they will always equal nine. Now turn to page 77. Do you see that all the answers add up to nine? If I said 5, what number would you add to it to make 9? Right! 4, so your answer would be 54." Turn to page 78 and read it to the students. Now put several 9 facts on the board and demonstrate the process to the class.

Teacher's Notes:
_____
_____
_____

Nines are the most fun of all because they are so easy to figure out.

MOMMY, WHAT DOES 'FIGGER' MEAN?

IT MEANS TO FIND THE ANSWER, HONEY, BY THINKING REAL HARD.

Book for Kids Page 73

First, take a look at the nines. What do you notice?

9	9	9
x1	x2	x3
9	18	27

9	9	9
x4	x5	x6
36	45	54

9	9	9
x7	x8	x9
63	72	81

You might have noticed one or both of the following:

Book for Kids Page 74

"TIMES TABLES THE FUN WAY"
Teacher's Manual

First, the answer always starts with one less than the number that nine is multiplied by.

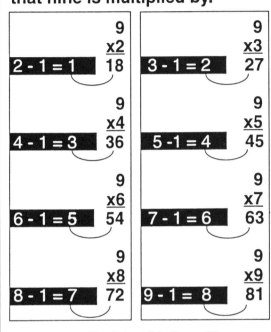

```
        9
       x2
2 - 1 = 1   18

        9
       x4
4 - 1 = 3   36

        9
       x6
6 - 1 = 5   54

        9
       x8
8 - 1 = 7   72
```

```
        9
       x3
3 - 1 = 2   27

        9
       x5
5 - 1 = 4   45

        9
       x7
7 - 1 = 6   63

        9
       x9
9 - 1 = 8   81
```

Book for Kids Page 75

The second thing you might have noticed is: if you add up the digits in the answer, they will always equal nine.

MOMMY, WHAT'S A 'DIGIT'?

IT'S A NUMBER, HONEY.

Book for Kids Page 76

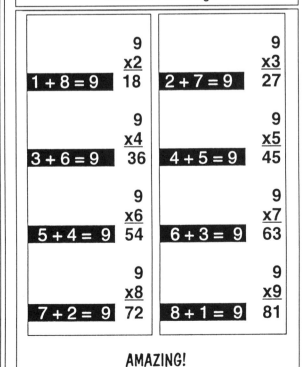

```
        9
       x2
1 + 8 = 9   18

        9
       x4
3 + 6 = 9   36

        9
       x6
5 + 4 = 9   54

        9
       x8
7 + 2 = 9   72
```

```
        9
       x3
2 + 7 = 9   27

        9
       x5
4 + 5 = 9   45

        9
       x7
6 + 3 = 9   63

        9
       x9
8 + 1 = 9   81
```

AMAZING!
Book for Kids Page 77

Now that we know these two <u>important</u> things about nines, let's try one.

What is 9 x 6 ?

First, ask yourself, what is one number less that 6?

Right! It's 5.

Second, ask yourself, what number when added to 5, will equal nine?

Right again! It's 4, because 5 + 4 = 9. So, your answer is 54.

Book for Kids Page 78

"TIMES TABLES THE FUN WAY"
Teacher's Manual

Topic:
Teach The Nines: Finger Folding Method

Goals:
Students will learn how to find the answers to the nine times tables by finger folding.

Material:
TTTFW Student Text Pages 79 - 81

Activity:
Students read along in the text while the teacher explains. Have all the students try the examples on page 81 and go around the classroom, looking at students' hands to make sure they understand. The Finger Folding Method should be used as a stepping stone to the adding method above.

The Finger Folding Method helps students see the pattern that occurs in the nine times tables. However, it is too time consuming to be used while figuring out facts for more complicated operations like double digit multiplication, simple division etc. Therefore, the adding method should be encouraged.

The Adding Method is practiced in the workbook pages, "Learning Nines". They are assigned in the next section.

Now let's try another method!

MOMMY, WHAT'S A 'METHOD'?

IT'S A WAY TO DO THINGS, HONEY.

Hold out your hands on the table-top.

Book for Kids Page 79

Let's try 9 x 6.

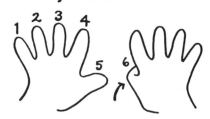

Start at the left and count to 6. Fold that finger down.

Look at what's left - 5 fingers and 4 fingers. Your answer is 54. AMAZING! 9 x 6 = 54

Book for Kids Page 80

"TIMES TABLES THE FUN WAY"
Teacher's Manual

Now, just for practice while your hands are still spread out on the table, try these:

9	9	9	9
x7	x9	x8	x4

Got it? Good.

Which method do you like the best?

Book for Kids Page 81

❖ **Section 3 - 3** *Practicing Nines and Around the World Game*

Topic:
Learning Nines Worksheet

Goals:
Students will become adept at figuring out the answers to the nines.

Material: TTTFW Workbook Pages 17 & 18

Activity:
Teacher may walk around classroom giving individual help as needed.

"TIMES TABLES THE FUN WAY"
WORKBOOK Lesson 3
LEARNING NINES

First, write down the number that is one less. Sample: What is one less than 5 ? Right! It's 4, so put a 4 in the blank $\boxed{5 \ \underline{4}}$

3___ 7___ 8___ 6___ 4___ 5___ 9___ 2___

Now, write down the number that you would add to make nine. Sample: $\boxed{3 \ \underline{6}}$
Because 3 + 6 = 9.

2___ 4___ 5___ 6___ 9___ 7___ 8___ 3___

On the next page, we will put these two steps together like this:

1. In the first space put the number that is one less than the number that nine is multiplied by:	2. In the space with the double line put the number that you would add to make nine (2 + 7 = 9, 3 + 6 = 9):
Sample:	**Sample:**
9 4	9 4
x3 x9	x3 x9
<u>2</u> <u>3</u>	<u>2 7</u> <u>3 6</u>

Go on to the next page

Student Workbook Page 17

"TIMES TABLES THE FUN WAY"
WORKBOOK Lesson 3
LEARNING NINES *Page Two*

Be careful!! Sometimes the number that nine is multiplied by is on top and sometimes its on the bottom. Always use the number that is not the nine to figure one less. (Except, of course, when it's 9 x 9.)

9	9	③	9	1	8	7
x7	x6	x9	x2	x9	x9	x9
6 3	5 4	2 7	___	___	___	___
	5+4=9	2+7=9				

9	9	6	9	7	9	9
x8	x1	x9	x9	x9	x5	x4
___	___	___	___	___	___	___

9	9	3	2	5	9	9
x3	x2	x9	x9	x9	x6	x9
___	___	___	___	___	___	___

9	8	9	9	5	9	9
x7	x9	x2	x4	x9	x9	x8
___	___	___	___	___	___	___

Congratulations! Now you know your nines!

Student Workbook Page 18

Answers:
TTTFW Teacher's Manual Page 69

"TIMES TABLES THE FUN WAY"
Teacher's Manual

Lesson 3

Topic:
Nines Timed Practice Sheet

Goal:
To finish the sheet as fast as possible and still score 100%

Material:
TTTFW Workbook - Page 19

Explanation:
"Try to fill in the answers as quickly as you can while taking care to be accurate. You will get a stamp for getting 100%, but you can also get a stamp for improving your own score. The object is to do it faster next time, to show that you are improving. It doesn't matter what time your neighbor gets, because you are competing with yourself not your neighbor. When you are done with the practice sheet, look at the clock and write your time down on the paper. I will write on the board when 1 minute has elapsed, 2 minutes, 3 minutes, etc. You write the minute and the seconds on your paper like this: 2:53. Be sure to put your time in the box marked time. When you are done with your sheet, just turn your workbook over and sit quietly. Do you have any questions? Is everyone ready? On your mark, get set GO."

Answers: TTTFW Teacher's Manual - Page 75

❖❖❖❖❖❖❖❖❖❖❖❖❖❖❖❖❖❖❖❖❖❖❖❖❖❖❖❖❖❖❖❖❖❖❖❖

Topic:
Game: Around the World

Goal:
Be one of the first three student to make it around the circle.

Set-up:
Sort two sets of *Times Tables The Fun Way* Flash Cards from lessons 1

"TIMES TABLES THE FUN WAY"
WORKBOOK Lesson 3
NINES TIMED PRACTICE

correct: | % score:
20

NAME_____ DATE_____ TIME_____

9 x 5	8 x 9	4 x 9	9 x 9
3 x 9	6 x 9	9 x 7	9 x 1
2 x 9	9 x 4	5 x 9	9 x 2
9 x 8	9 x 6	7 x 9	9 x 3
7 x 7	4 x 3	8 x 8	6 x 4

Student Workbook Page 19

through 3. Divide class into two groups. Select two team captains, one for each group .

Activity:
Students sit in a circle. Determine a starting person in the circle. This person stands directly behind the person to his left. The captain flashes a card to both students. The first one to say the answer advances to the next position around the circle. The loser sits down and the winner advances around the circle. Continue until three students have made it around the circle (world). These students should receive a Won Game Stamp on the Stamp / Score Sheet.

❖•❖

Topic:
Issue Stamps

Material:
TTTFW Workbook - Page 45: Score Sheet

Activity:
Ask students to bring workbooks up to the teacher so stamps can be issued. When a student has accumulated 10 stamps, they can be given a coupon. Two coupons can be used as a Homework Pass, (no homework due for one assignment of the student's choice, or other rewards as determined by the teacher.)

Material:
TTTFW Teacher's Manual - Page 98: Awards. Make copies and cut apart.

"TIMES TABLES THE FUN WAY"
STAMP AND SCORE SUMMARY SHEET

Lesson 1	Lesson 2	Lesson 3	Lesson 4
Pre-test	Quiz # 1	Quiz # 2	Quiz # 3
Score: ___	Facts: ___ Stories: ___	Facts: ___ Stories: ___	Facts: ___ Stories: ___
Time: ___			
	Fives Practice	1's & 2's Practice	Fives Practice
1's & 2's Practice	Score: ___	Score: ___	Score: ___
Score: ___	Time: ___	Time: ___	Time: ___
Time: ___			
		Nines Practice	
		Score: ___	
		Time: ___	
Stamps:	Stamps:	Stamps:	Stamps:

Lesson 5	Lesson 6	Lesson 7	Lesson 8
Quiz # 4	Quiz # 5	Quiz # 6	Post-test
Facts: ___ Stories: ___	Facts: ___ Stories: ___	Facts: ___ Stories: ___	Score: ___
			Time: ___
Nines Practice	Fives Practice	Homework Quiz	
Score: ___	Score: ___	Score: ___	
Time: ___	Time: ___		
		Nines Practice	
Story Quiz		Score: ___	
Facts: ___ Stories: ___		Time: ___	
Stamps:	Stamps:	Stamps:	Stamps:

Student Workbook Page 45

Teacher's Notes:
_____
_____
_____
_____

"TIMES TABLES THE FUN WAY"
Teacher's Manual

Section 4 - 1 *Quiz and Musical Fives*

Topic:
Quiz #3...give 5 minutes to complete

Goal:
Students will remember stories that go with the facts so that they can illustrate them. Give clues if necessary.

Explanation:
You will have five minutes to complete the quiz. You will not be recording your time so you don't have to try to hurry. Just try to finish it in five minutes.

Material:
TTTFW Workbook - Page 20

Answers:
TTTFW Teacher's Manual - Page 69

```
"TIMES TABLES THE FUN WAY"
        WORKBOOK Lesson 4
QUIZ # 3  NAME_____ DATE_____

Answer these facts:
 6    6    5    6    9    7    8    4
x3   x8   x5   x5   x9   x9   x5   x9      # CORRECT
                                            ┌──┐
                                            │ 8│
                                            └──┘
What is the story for 6 x 3 ?  Draw it or write it.




                                          # CORRECT
                                            ┌──┐
                                            │ 1│
                                            └──┘
- - - - - - - - - - - - - - - - - - - - -
What is the story for 6 x 8 ?  Draw it or write it.




                                          # CORRECT
                                            ┌──┐
                                            │ 1│
                                            └──┘
```
Student Workbook Page 20

Topic:
Musical Fives

Goal:
To practice the five facts and be able to determine the factors for the answers to the fact.

Material:
TTTFW Teacher's Manual
Page 87: Musical Fives Answer Cards, one set per group

Set-up:
Divide into groups of 5-7 students. Form group circles.

Teacher's Notes:
_____
_____
_____
_____
_____
_____
_____
_____
_____
_____
_____

"TIMES TABLES THE FUN WAY"
Teacher's Manual

Start at one point in the circle. Team captains can be selected by asking the groups whose birthday is coming up next. Each captain should be given the answers to Musical Fives.

Activity:

Students count by fives. Each student saying one number. Teacher plays music from a record player, tape cassette, or radio. Teacher turns the music off at random intervals. When the music stops, the one who gave the last answer has 5 seconds to say the number that five is multiplied by. Teacher should announce that time is up. i.e. student says 35 when music goes off, he has five seconds to say 7 x 5 = 35. If the student misses, he is given a token by the team captain, but he continues to play. The students with no tokens at the end of the game are the winners and they can recieve a Won Game Stamp.

Topic:

Fives Timed Practice Sheet

Goal:

To finish the sheet as fast as possible and still score100%

Explanation:

"OK, now we are going to do the Fives Timed Practice Sheet again. Be sure to go as fast as you can and try to beat your last time and score on the Fives Sheet. When you are done, write down your time and work on any of your unfinished workbook pages but don't work ahead of page 21. Everyone ready? Ok, you may begin."

Material:

TTTFW Workbook - Page 21

"TIMES TABLES THE FUN WAY"
WORKBOOK Lesson 4
FIVES TIMED PRACTICE

correct: % score:
          20

NAME_____ DATE_____ TIME____

1 x 5	5 x 5	9 x 5	5 x 4
6 x 5	4 x 5	8 x 5	5 x 3
7 x 5	3 x 5	5 x 2	5 x 8
5 x 1	5 x 9	5 x 6	5 x 7
3 x 3	4 x 3	8 x 8	7 x 7

Student Workbook Page 21

"TIMES TABLES THE FUN WAY"
Teacher's Manual

Topic:
Grading The Fives Practice Sheet

Material: TTTFW Workbook - Page 21

Activity:
Class exchanges books and fills out Stamp / Score Sheet

Answers:
TTTFW Teacher's Manual - Page 74: Grading Template

❖❖❖❖❖❖❖❖❖❖❖❖❖❖❖❖❖❖❖❖❖❖❖❖❖❖❖❖❖❖❖❖❖❖❖

Section 4 - 2   *Division: Splitting Into Groups, The Butterfly Story*

Topic:
Teach Division

Goals:
Students will understand that division is "dividing into groups." They will be able to answer the division problems based on the multiplication facts already learned.

Explanation:
"You have learned many multiplication facts already. You know your fives, your nines, twos, ones, and some of the sixes, sevens, and eights. If you know these facts, then you can do division. Division is backwards multiplication. Let me give you an example: We just played a game called Musical Fives. How many people were in each group? Answer: about 5 and there are 30 students in the class. So, 30 divided by 6 groups gives 5 students for each group. Division simply means, "to split into groups". Now let me show you how you can turn a multiplication fact into a division problem. 7 x 8 = 56.
If I wrote 56 divided by 8 = ? You ask yourself, what number times 8 will give me 56. Right. The answer is 7.
Let's do some more:

"TIMES TABLES THE FUN WAY"
Teacher's Manual

(Put these problems on the board and ask students: what number times (4)___ will give you (20) ___?)

$$20 / 4 = \qquad 12 / 4 =$$
$$9 / 3 = \qquad 36 / 6 =$$
$$16 / 4 = \qquad 25 / 5 =$$
$$64 / 8 = \qquad 48 / 8 =$$
$$49 / 7 = \qquad 18 / 3 =$$

❖❖

Topic:
Learning Division

Material:
TTTFW Workbook - Pages 22 and 23

Activity:
Students read the workbook and answer the questions.

"TIMES TABLES THE FUN WAY"
WORKBOOK Lesson 4
LEARNING DIVISION

Division is the opposite of multiplication. Here is a sample: $64 \div 8 = ?$

Ask yourself what number times 8 will give you 64. Right! The answer is 8 because $8 \times 8 = 64$.

Here's another one: $56 \div 7 = ?$
What number times 7 will give you 56? Right! The answer is 8 because $7 \times 8 = 56$

Try these:

$25 \div 5 =$ _____ (*Think: $25 = 5 \times$?*)
$12 \div 3 =$ _____ (*Think: $12 = 3 \times$?*)
$16 \div 4 =$ _____ (*Think: $16 = 4 \times$?*)
$18 \div 3 =$ _____ (*Think: $18 = 3 \times$?*)
$30 \div 6 =$ _____ (*Think: $30 = 6 \times$?*)
$49 \div 7 =$ _____ (*Think: $49 = 7 \times$?*)
$81 \div 9 =$ _____ (*Think: $81 = 9 \times$?*)
$40 \div 5 =$ _____ (*Think: $40 = 5 \times$?*)

Go on to the next page

Student Workbook Page 22

"TIMES TABLES THE FUN WAY"
WORKBOOK Lesson 4
LEARNING DIVISION PAGE TWO

There is another way to write division problems. They look like this:

$$6\overline{)36}$$

When you see a problem like this, you ask yourself: What number times 6 equals 36, or $6 \times ? = 36$. The answer is 6 because $6 \times 6 = 36$. So, put the 6 on top of the house.

$$6$$
$$6\overline{)36}$$

Now try these:

$$4\overline{)16} \qquad 3\overline{)12} \qquad 5\overline{)40} \qquad 9\overline{)72} \qquad 3\overline{)18}$$

Go on to the next page

Student Workbook Page 23

❖❖

Teacher's Notes:

_____
_____
_____
_____
_____
_____

"TIMES TABLES THE FUN WAY"
Teacher's Manual

Lesson 4

Topic:
Worksheet #2
Material:
TTTFW Workbook - Page 24
Activity:
Students practice double digit multiplication and their newly learned skill: division
Answers:
TTTFW Teacher's Manual - Page 69

◆◆◆◆◆◆◆◆◆◆◆◆◆◆◆◆◆◆◆◆◆◆◆

Topic:
Teach Story 3 x 7
Discussion:

"Do you know what happens when a caterpillar spins a cocoon? How long does it take the cocoon to open? Why do you think nature makes butterflies start from a caterpillar. Why don't butterflies just have butterfly babies?"

Material: TTTFW Student Text Pages 52 - 53

"TIMES TABLES THE FUN WAY"
WORKBOOK Lesson 4
WORKSHEET # 2

46	16	56	58	36
x6	x8	x6	x6	x3

64	62	18	27	88
x6	x6	x7	x7	x5

6⟌36   3⟌12   8⟌48   9⟌81   8⟌56

3⟌18   7⟌49   7⟌56   5⟌40   9⟌72

9⟌63   9⟌54   9⟌27   5⟌25   6⟌18

Student Workbook Page 24

$3 \times 7 = 21$

There is a special tree in a far away land. It is called the Seven Tree. It is a hatching place for many butterflies. The butterflies start out as caterpillars. When they are ready, they spin a cocoon and hang from a leaf on the special Seven Tree. Soon each cocoon turns into a butterfly.

Each time a new butterfly is born, it flies around the tree and waits for a partner to hatch. When the butterfly finds a friend, they fly off to a flower patch and settle down to a peaceful life.

Book for Kids Page 52

Remember: When 3 is with 7, 3 is a butterfly at the 7 tree. The caterpillar (2) will soon become a cocoon (1).

Book for Kids Page 53

Page 40

"TIMES TABLES THE FUN WAY"
Teacher's Manual

Section 4 - 3 *Burning Barn Story and Duck Goose Game*

Topic: Teach Story 7 x 4

Discussion: "What should you do if a fire starts at your house? Have you ever seen a house on fire? What are some safety pointers to avoid starting fires?"

Material:

TTTFW Student Text Pages 54-55

> **7 x 4 = 28**
>
> 7 is a fireman at the 7 x 4th Street Station. The bell rings and wakes 7 out of a sound sleep. He puts on his hat and boots and rushes to the fire pole. 7 slides down the pole as fast as he can and gets into the fire truck.
>
> After traveling for a long time, 7 finally arrives at Farmer John's barn. The farmer has been very busy saving the animals. Farmer John says to the 7 fireman, "I'm afraid you're too late. I got the animals out, but the barn is nearly burned to the ground."
>
> Book for Kids Page 54

Remember: When 7 is with 4, 7 is a fireman and 4 is the fire pole. They arrive at the fire too (2) late (8).

Book for Kids Page 55

Topic: Worksheet #2a

Goal: Practice introduced facts

Material: TTTFW Workbook Page 25

Activity: Students complete worksheet while teacher walks around room giving individual help. Students that finish before the others can tutor their peers.

Answers: TTTFW Teacher's Manual Pg. 70

"TIMES TABLES THE FUN WAY"
WORKBOOK Lesson 4
WORKSHEET # 2a

26	28	65	65	33
x6	x6	x6	x8	x7

46	27	17	47	97
x6	x4	x8	x7	x5

6)30	7)28	8)56	8)40	8)72

6)18	4)12	6)48	6)36	7)56

3)21	7)49	9)36	5)45	3)18

Student Workbook Page 25

"TIMES TABLES THE FUN WAY"
Teacher's Manual

Topic:
Game: Duck Duck Goose

Goal:
Reinforce the introduced facts in a game format with physical activity.

Material:
Times Tables The Fun Way Flash Cards from Lessons 1 through 4, one set for each group.

Set-up:
Divide into groups of 4 or 5 students. Select a captain for each group. Select a goose for each group.

Activity:
Students sit in a circle on the floor while "the goose" goes around tapping each student on the head saying "duck." Within two rounds the student must select an opponent by saying "goose" when he taps the opponent's head. The team captain now shows a flash card to the goose and the tapper. The first one to say the answer to the fact is the new goose. The captain should give the winner a token. The new goose now becomes the tapper and the old tapper sits down. The new goose must choose someone that has not been the goose before. This method allows everyone to get a chance. The winner is the person with the most tokens. Give a Won Game stamp to the winners on their Stamp and Score Sheet.

Teacher's Notes:
_____
_____
_____
_____
_____
_____
_____

Section 4 - 4
Worksheet And Giant Tic Tac Toe
Topic:
Worksheet #2b

Goal:
Practice introduced facts

Material: TTTFW Workbook - Page 26

Activity: Students complete worksheet while teacher walks around room giving individual help. Students that finish before the others can tutor their peers.
Answers: TTTFW Teacher's Manual Pg. 70

"TIMES TABLES THE FUN WAY"
WORKBOOK Lesson 4
WORKSHEET # 2b

46	26	58	56	23
x5	x8	x7	x8	x3

66	26	27	55	38
x5	x6	x7	x7	x6

5⟌30   7⟌49   6⟌48   5⟌40   7⟌56

3⟌18   4⟌12   8⟌56   9⟌81   8⟌72

7⟌63   6⟌54   3⟌27   5⟌15   6⟌18

Student Workbook Page 26

❖❖

Topic:
Giant Story Tic Tac Toe

Goal:
To reinforce the story number connection. The object of the game is to be the first team to fill in all the squares with the answers and the correct story clue. (Shorter version: winning team makes the first tic tac toe, 3 correct in a row, column, or diagonal.)

Set-up:

Put two large tic tac toe squares on the blackboard. Fill in each square with the following facts and make a

7 x 7 =	8 x 8 =	6 x 6 =	Snail Butterfly Soldiers Cake Fire Bouncy Guy Desert Hunter Snowmen	7 x 7 =	8 x 8 =	6 x 6 =
8 x 7 =	6 x 3 =	6 x 4 =		8 x 7 =	6 x 3 =	6 x 4 =
7 x 4 =	6 x 8 =	3 x 7 =		7 x 4 =	6 x 8 =	3 x 7 =

column with the clue words in the middle as illustrated above.
Draw two starting lines with masking tape on the rug. Divide the class into two teams. Have the teams form single file lines behind the masking tape.

"TIMES TABLES THE FUN WAY"
Teacher's Manual

Activity:

Play begins when the first person in each line comes up to their team's tic tac toe square and selects a box to answer. This person puts the answer to the fact and the clue that goes with that fact's story. Player runs back to the head of their line and tags the next person, who then comes up and answers a box. Students get only one try. If they guess incorrectly, they go to the end of the line. Students should be encouraged to look up the answers in their books while they are waiting, if necessary. The first team to fill in all the squares is the winning team. Give a stamp to each person on the winning team.

❖❖❖❖❖❖❖❖❖❖❖❖❖❖❖❖❖❖❖❖❖❖❖❖❖❖❖❖❖❖❖❖❖❖❖

Topic:
Issue Stamps

Material:
TTTFW Workbook - Page 45: Score Sheet

Activity:

Ask students to bring workbooks up to the teacher so stamps can be issued. When a student has accumulated 10 stamps, they can be given a coupon. Two coupons can be used as a Homework Pass, (no homework due for one assignment of the student's choice, or other rewards as determined by the teacher.)

Material:
TTTFW Teacher's Manual - Page 98: Awards. Make copies and cut apart.

Student Workbook Page 45

❖❖❖❖❖❖❖❖❖❖❖❖❖❖❖❖❖❖❖❖❖❖❖❖❖❖❖❖❖❖❖❖❖❖❖

Teacher's Notes:

_____

_____

_____

_____

"TIMES TABLES THE FUN WAY"
Teacher's Manual

Section 5 - 1   *Story Review, Quiz, And The High Jump Contest*

Topic:
Review The Stories

Goal:
To solidify the story number connection. Object: Don't be the last student to take a token out of the pot or you'll have to act out the story.

Material:
Two sets of *Times Tables The Fun Way* cards from lessons 1 through 4. Sort the cards so that only the ones with the story characters are used, (9 cards total).

Set-up:
Divide the class into two groups. Select a captain for each group. The captain should know the stories. Put three tokens in a pot in the middle of the group. The captain shows the first card to one student. The student must tell the story and say the fact and the answer. Proceed to the next student moving in clockwise fashion. If a student forgets the story, take a token out of the middle. Then, have that student turn to the story page in the student text and read the story out loud. When the third token is taken out of the pot, the captain should quickly summarize the story and the answer to that fact. Then, the captain should secretly show the student the next card. The student must now act out the story trying to get the group to guess the story and the fact. If the group guesses correctly, put three more tokens in the middle and proceed. If the group does not guess the story, the captain has the next student act out the story for the next card. Play proceeds until the 9 story cards have been used twice.

❖❖❖❖❖❖❖❖❖❖❖❖❖❖❖❖❖❖❖❖❖❖❖❖❖❖❖❖❖❖❖❖❖❖❖❖

Teacher's Notes:
_____
_____
_____
_____

"TIMES TABLES THE FUN WAY"
Teacher's Manual

Topic:
Quiz #4..give 5 minutes to complete
Goal:
Students will remember stories that go with the facts so that they can illustrate them. Give clues if necessary.
Explanation:
"You will have five minutes to complete the quiz. You will not be recording your time so you don't have to try to hurry. Just try to finish it in five minutes."
Material: TTTFW Workbook - Page 27
Answers: TTTFW Teacher's Manual Pg. 69

❖◇❖◇❖◇❖◇❖◇❖◇❖◇❖◇❖◇❖◇❖◇❖

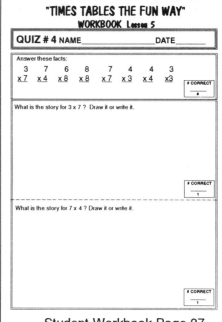

"TIMES TABLES THE FUN WAY"
WORKBOOK Lesson 5

QUIZ # 4 NAME_____ DATE_____

Answer these facts:

3	7	6	8	7	4	4	3
x7	x4	x8	x8	x7	x3	x4	x3

CORRECT

What is the story for 3 x 7 ? Draw it or write it.

CORRECT

What is the story for 7 x 4 ? Draw it or write it.

CORRECT

Student Workbook Page 27

Topic: Teach Story 7 x 6
Discussion: "Do you ever have contests with your friends? Do you like to compete? Why or why not?"
Material: TTTFW Student Text Pages 56 - 57

7 x 6 = 42
 7 and 6 are best friends. 7 is very very skinny and 6 is very very chubby. Whenever they get together to play, they invent contests to see who will win.
 They set up a high jump contest. 7 said, "I'll do it if you will go first." And 6 said, "OK, I'll go first but I'm going to put a cushion on the other side to land on. I don't want to break my fluffy body. Please give me a push," and away he went. 7 went next. Who do you think won the contest?

Book for Kids Page 56

Remember: When 7 is with 6 they have a high jump (4) contest and land on the cushion (2).

Book for Kids Page 57

Section 5 - 2   *Muddy Puddles, Nines, And Problem Practice*

Topic:
Teach Story 8 x 4

Discussion:
"Do you ever go outside and play in the rain? Is it safe to play outside if there is thunder and lightning around? What should you do if you are stuck in a lightning storm?" (Lay down in a ditch, do not hide under a single, lone tree.)

Material:
TTTFW Student Text Pages 64 - 65

8 x 4 = 32
There were two pigs that lived in a mountain town. One afternoon a huge thunderstorm poured rain for hours. When the sun finally came out, the two pigs ran outside to play. They were having fun making mud pies when their mom called them in for dinner. When she saw the pigs she said, "Little 8 pig, you go right upstairs and take a bath. You are so dirty." While the 8 pig was getting cleaned up she said, "Mom, why doesn't my brother have to take a bath? He's dirty too!"

Book for Kids Page 64

Remember: When 8 is with 4, 8 is the muddy pig and the 4 is the tub. The pig says, "He's dirty too". (32)

Book for Kids Page 65

Teacher's Notes:

"TIMES TABLES THE FUN WAY"
Teacher's Manual

Topic:
Nines Timed Practice Sheet

Goal:
To improve score and / or time as compared to last performance on the Nines Timed Practice Sheet

Explanation:
"OK, now we are going to do the Nines Timed Practice Sheet again. Be sure to go as fast as you can and try to beat your last time and score on the Nines Practice Sheet. When you are done, write down your time and work on any of your unfinished workbook pages but don't work ahead of page 28. Everyone ready? Ok, Go."

Material:
TTTFW Workbook - Page 28

❖❖❖❖❖❖❖❖❖❖❖❖❖❖❖❖❖❖❖❖❖❖❖❖❖❖❖❖❖❖❖

Topic:
Grading The Nines Practice Sheet

Material: TTTFW Workbook - Page 28

Activity:
Class exchanges books and fills out Stamp / Score Sheet.

Answers: TTTFW Teacher's Manual - Pg.75: Grading Template

❖❖❖❖❖❖❖❖❖❖❖❖❖❖❖❖❖❖❖❖❖❖❖❖❖❖❖❖❖❖❖

Topic:
Worksheet #3 and #3a
Goal:
Practice introduced facts

"TIMES TABLES THE FUN WAY"
WORKBOOK Lesson 5
NINES TIMED PRACTICE

# correct:	% score:
	20

NAME_____ DATE_____ TIME_____

9 x 5	8 x 9	4 x 9	9 x 9
3 x 9	6 x 9	9 x 7	9 x 1
2 x 9	9 x 4	5 x 9	9 x 2
9 x 8	9 x 6	7 x 9	9 x 3
7 x 7	4 x 3	8 x 8	6 x 4

Student Workbook Page 28

Teacher's Notes:
_____
_____
_____
_____
_____

"TIMES TABLES THE FUN WAY"
Teacher's Manual

Material:
TTTFW Workbook Pg. 29,30
Activity:
Students complete worksheet while teacher walks around room giving individual help. Students that finish before the others can tutor their peers.
Answers: TTTFW T. Man. Pg. 70

"TIMES TABLES THE FUN WAY"
WORKBOOK Lesson 5
WORKSHEET # 3

47	56	54	55	46
x6	x3	x3	x5	x4
28	66	58	44	64
x7	x6	x5	x4	x5
73	36	36	76	82
x5	x4	x3	x5	x5

9⟌63   9⟌54   9⟌27   5⟌25   3⟌18

21÷3 =   25÷5 =

56÷7 =   30÷6 =

Student Workbook Page 29

"TIMES TABLES THE FUN WAY"
WORKBOOK Lesson 5
WORKSHEET # 3a

56	65	24	95	64
x7	x3	x8	x5	x6
26	67	85	24	55
x6	x6	x5	x4	x5
37	63	37	56	28
x5	x4	x3	x7	x4

7⟌56   6⟌42   3⟌27   5⟌30   6⟌18

21÷3 =   30 ÷5 =

45÷9 =   42 ÷6 =

Student Workbook Page 30

❖❖❖❖❖❖❖❖❖❖❖❖❖❖❖❖❖❖❖❖❖❖❖❖❖❖❖❖❖❖❖❖❖❖❖❖

Section 5 - 3   *Story, Story, What's The Story?*

Topic:
Story Quiz...give 6 minutes to complete

Goal:
To complete the page, remembering as many as possible.

Activity:
Students write down one or two key words about the story to show that they know it. Students do as many as they can. When they are finished, they exchange workbooks while teacher reads the answers. Students circle the blank, or incorrect stories. Students should put the number correct in the upper right hand corner of the page and give the workbook back to the owner. Now students should look up the answers that they missed and fill them in.

"TIMES TABLES THE FUN WAY"
WORKBOOK Lesson 5

STORY QUIZ Write the answer and one or two words about the story.

Stories
# correct:	% score:
11	

Facts
# correct:	% score:
11	

	ANSWER
1. 7 X 7 =	
2. 6 X 7 =	
3. 8 X 8 =	
4. 6 X 4 =	
5. 6 X 6 =	
6. 6 X 8 =	
7. 3 X 7 =	
8. 8 X 7 =	
9. 8 X 4 =	
10. 7 X 4 =	
11. 6 X 3 =	

Student Workbook Page 31

"TIMES TABLES THE FUN WAY"
Teacher's Manual

Lesson 5

Students that complete the page and / or received 100% can get a stamp on the Stamp / Score Sheet.

Material: TTTFW Workbook - Page 31

Answers: TTTFW Teacher's Manual - Page 70

❖◆❖◆❖◆❖◆❖◆❖◆❖◆❖◆❖◆❖◆❖◆❖◆❖◆❖◆❖◆❖◆❖◆❖◆

Topic:
Worksheet # 3b

Goal:
To practice the introduced facts

Material: TTTFW Workbook - Page 32

Activity:
Students complete worksheet while teacher walks around room giving individual help. Students that finish before the others can tutor their peers.

Answers: TTTFW Teacher's Manual - Page 70

> **"TIMES TABLES THE FUN WAY"**
> **WORKBOOK Lesson 5**
> **WORKSHEET # 3b**
>
> | 67 | 36 | 44 | 55 | 46 |
> |----|----|----|----|----|
> | x4 | x5 | x3 | x5 | x6 |
>
> | 33 | 67 | 58 | 48 | 67 |
> |----|----|----|----|----|
> | x7 | x6 | x5 | x4 | x6 |
>
> | 78 | 36 | 36 | 76 | 82 |
> |----|----|----|----|----|
> | x4 | x4 | x3 | x4 | x5 |
>
> 8⟌32   7⟌28   6⟌42   3⟌21   6⟌18
>
> 32÷4 =   35÷5 =
>
> 56÷8 =   48÷6 =
>
> Student Workbook Page 32

❖◆❖◆❖◆❖◆❖◆❖◆❖◆❖◆❖◆❖◆❖◆❖◆❖◆❖◆❖◆❖◆❖◆❖◆

Topic:
Game: Name That Story: Game Two

Goal:
To be the first one to say the story and the answer to the fact. To reinforce the story number connection using all the stories that have been introduced.

Material:
TTTFW Teacher's Manual
Pages 80-83: Name That Story Game Two Cards. Make copies on card stock: one set per group.

Activity:

Show the cards to the class, one by one. The first person to say the story that goes along with the fact and the whole fact with the answer wins. Give a point to that person. The students with the top points will be the team captains. Now divide into groups of 2-6 kids. Arrange seats in a circle. The team captain shows a card to the first two students. They race to say the answer. The first one to say the story and the whole fact gets a point. Chips or tokens can be given to keep track of points. The captain then shows the next card to the next two students.

Continue around the circle until all the cards have been used 2 times. The student with the most points is the winner. Example: Card is 7 x 7, student says, "There are two soldiers on litter patrol so 7 x 7 = 49". Students must say the whole fact and at least one word from the story to show they know it. Captains should switch positions of students so that the winners sit next to each other and must compete amongst themselves, this gives every one a chance for a point.

At the end of the session, students that won their group session should get a stamp on their Stamp and Score sheet, and captains should also receive a stamp in the box marked: Won Game.

❖❖❖❖❖❖❖❖❖❖❖❖❖❖❖❖❖❖❖❖❖❖❖❖❖❖❖❖❖❖❖❖❖❖❖

Topic:
Homework Study
Activity:

Remind students that there will be a homework test at the next lesson. They should study all of the facts, except 3 x 8, which will be taught at the next lesson. Make sure each student brings home a book to study for the homework test at the next session.

❖❖❖❖❖❖❖❖❖❖❖❖❖❖❖❖❖❖❖❖❖❖❖❖❖❖❖❖❖❖❖❖❖❖❖

Topic:
Issue Stamps
Material: TTTFW Workbook - Page 45: Score Sheet
Activity: Ask students to bring workbooks up to the teacher so stamps can be issued. Give coupons to students that have accumulated 10 stamps.
Awards: TTTFW Teacher's Manual: Awards Pg 90: Make copies and cut apart

"TIMES TABLES THE FUN WAY"
Teacher's Manual

Section 6 - 1   *Quiz, King Of Snakes, And The Fine Fives*

Topic:
Quiz #5 ...give 5 minutes to complete.

Goal:
Students score 100% on the stories & the facts.

Explanation:
"You will have five minutes to complete the quiz. You will not be recording your time so you don't have to try to hurry. Just try to finish it in five minutes."

Material:TTTFW Workbook - Page 33

Answers:TTTFW Teacher' Manual - Page 69

❖❖❖❖❖❖❖❖❖❖❖❖❖❖❖❖❖❖❖❖❖❖

Topic: Teach Story 8 x 3

Discussion:"Does anyone know what spalunking is? (cave exploring) Has anyone ever done it? Did you know that it is very dangerous to enter old mines or caves? Why?" (get lost, mines can collapse, etc.)   **Material:**TTTFW Student Text Page 62 - 63

"TIMES TABLES THE FUN WAY"
WORKBOOK Lesson 6

QUIZ #5 NAME_____ DATE_____

Answer these facts:

| 8 | 7 | 3 | 7 | 6 | 6 | 8 | 6 | |
|x4|x6|x7|x4|x8|x3|x7|x4| # CORRECT |

What is the story for 7 x 6 ? Draw it or write it.

CORRECT

What is the story for 8 x 4 ? Draw it or write it.

CORRECT

Student Workbook Page 33

---

3 x 8 = 24

There was a huge bat that loved to explore caves at night. He had been flying into caves for many years.

One time the bat found a hibernating bear and one time he found a very awake cougar. But the scariest adventure of all was when he flew into the cave by the Black Lagoon.

To the bat's surprise, he found the King of Snakes sitting on a throne. The bat was so scared he flew right out as fast as he flew in!

Book for Kids Page 62

Remember: When 3 is with 8, 3 is a bat who flies into the cave (8) and finds the King of Snakes (2) on a throne (4).

Book for Kids Page 63

"TIMES TABLES THE FUN WAY"
Teacher's Manual

Topic:

Fives Timed Practice Sheet

Goal:

To improve last score and time on the Fives Timed Practice Sheet.

Explanation:

"OK, now we are going to do the Fives Timed Practice Sheet again. Be sure to go as fast as you can and try to beat your last time and score on the Fives Sheet. When you are done, write down your time and work on any of your unfinished workbook pages but don't work ahead of page 34. Everyone ready? Ok, Go."

Material:

TTTFW Workbook - Page 34

"TIMES TABLES THE FUN WAY"
WORKBOOK Lesson 6
FIVES TIMED PRACTICE

# correct:	% score:
20	

NAME_____ DATE_____ TIME_____

1 x 5	5 x 5	9 x 5	5 x 4
6 x 5	4 x 5	8 x 5	5 x 3
7 x 5	3 x 5	5 x 2	5 x 8
5 x 1	5 x 9	5 x 6	5 x 7
3 x 3	4 x 3	8 x 8	7 x 7

Student Workbook Page 34

Topic:

Grading The Fives Practice Sheet

Material:

TTTFW Workbook - Page 34

Activity:

Class exchanges books and fills out Stamp / Score Sheet

Answers: TTTFW Teacher's Manual - Page 74: Grading Template

Section 6 - 2 *Problem Practice And Pantomime Time*

Topic:

Worksheet #4 and #4a

Goal:

To practice the introduced facts

Material:

TTTFW Workbook - Page 35 and 36

Teacher's Notes: _____
_____
_____

"TIMES TABLES THE FUN WAY"
WORKBOOK Lesson 6
WORKSHEET # 4

43	55	77	88	99
x8	x7	x6	x4	x3
77	33	46	36	46
x4	x7	x8	x3	x6
88	78	66	57	43
x7	x8	x4	x7	x3

36÷6 =   35÷5 =

81÷9 =   48÷6 =

Student Workbook Page 35

Lesson 6

Activity:
Students complete worksheet while teacher walks around room giving individual help. Students that finish before the others can tutor their peers.

Answers:
TTTFW Teacher's Manual - Page 70

❖◆❖◆❖◆❖◆❖◆❖◆❖◆❖◆❖◆❖◆❖◆

Topic:
Game: Pantomime Story Time
Goal:
Guess the fact based on the student's actions of the story.

Material:
TTTFW Teacher's Manual - Pages 84-87: Pantomime Story Time Game Cards. Make copies on cardstock, if necessary, and cut cards apart.
Activity:

Divide into groups of 5 - 7 students. Select a captain for each group. The captain shows the first card to a student. The student whispers the story to the captain to show that he knows which story goes with the fact. The student then acts out the story (silently) while the other group members guess the fact. If the actor does not know the story for that fact, the captain gives him a slip of paper with the fact on it. The missed card is put at the bottom of the Pantomime Card pile. The actor gets one more try with the next card. If he still doesn't know the story, he gets another slip of paper with the missed fact and sits down.

Every time a student guesses the correct fact, the guesser receives a token and so does the actor. Each actor has a time limit of one minute. If no one guesses the story in 1 minute, no one gets a token. At the end of the game, the students with slips of paper must look up the story in the book and then act it out for the others to guess. They also must give up one token for each slip of paper. The student with the most tokens receives a Won Game stamp on the Stamp / Score Sheet.

"TIMES TABLES THE FUN WAY"
WORKBOOK Lesson 6
WORKSHEET # 4a

38	77	67	98	33
x4	x5	x6	x4	x9
74	23	64	66	47
x6	x7	x8	x3	x6
82	39	72	58	53
x8	x8	x4	x7	x3

$63 \div 9 =$ $35 \div 7 =$

$72 \div 9 =$ $48 \div 8 =$

Student Workbook Page 36

"TIMES TABLES THE FUN WAY"
Teacher's Manual

Lesson 6

Section 6 - 3 *Perfect Practice, Homework Test, Advancement*
Topic:
Worksheet #4b
Goal:
Practice introduced facts
Material:
TTTFW Workbook - Page 37
Activity:
Students complete worksheet while teacher walks around room giving individual help. Students that finish before the others can tutor their peers.
Answers:
TTTFW Teacher's Manual - Page 70

"TIMES TABLES THE FUN WAY"
WORKBOOK Lesson 6
WORKSHEET # 4b

84	57	87	89	49
x3	x7	x6	x4	x3

47	38	69	96	46
x4	x3	x8	x3	x5

92	87	65	54	49
x7	x8	x4	x7	x3

$48 \div 6 =$ $32 \div 8 =$

$72 \div 8 =$ $56 \div 7 =$

Student Workbook Page 37

Topic:
Homework Test...give 6 minutes to complete
Goal:
To determine which facts each student needs to review.
Explanation:
"You will be taking the Homework Test now. You will have 6 minutes to complete it. If you score 100% on this test you won't have any homework. If you miss a few, these will be assigned for homework and you will have a quiz on the ones you missed at the next session. You will get a special award if you score 100% on the test today or on the homework quiz next session. Ok, is everyone ready? You may start."
Material:
TTTFW Workbook - Page 38

"TIMES TABLES THE FUN WAY"
WORKBOOK Lesson 6   Name:
HOMEWORK TEST   Date:

8	7	6	8	6	4	3	4	1
x8	x7	x4	x7	x6	x3	x3	x4	x1
2	3	2	2	2	5	1	4	1
x1	x2	x4	x2	x9	x2	x5	x1	x3
1	2	2	7	6	9	2	5	5
x7	x6	x8	x2	x1	x1	x9	x3	x5
5	5	8	5	5	6	6	3	7
x7	x9	x5	x6	x4	x3	x8	x7	x4
9	6	9	9	9	7	8	8	1
x4	x9	x7	x9	x8	x6	x4	x3	x8

After you have taken this test and graded it, tear this sheet out and learn the missed facts for your homework assignment. Next session, you will have a quiz on the ones you missed.

Student Workbook Page 38

Page 55

"TIMES TABLES THE FUN WAY"
Teacher's Manual

Lesson 6

Topic:
Grading The Homework Test

Explanation:
"Please exchange workbooks and I will read the answers. If the fact is incorrect, please put a check mark next to the answer. Ok, is everyone ready?" Teacher reads answers across the rows.

Material:
TTTFW Workbook - Page 38

Answers:
TTTFW Teacher's Manual - Page 77: Grading Template

Topic:
How Many Facts Do You Know?

Explanation:
"Please give workbooks back to their owners. Now everyone write down the facts you missed on the next workbook page, *How Many Facts Do You Know*? Be sure to just write the fact and NOT THE ANSWER. This sheet will be used for the Homework Quiz at the next session. Tear out the Homework Test and take it home in order to study the ones you missed. Your homework is to learn the ones you missed by the next session. Remember, if you score 100% on the Homework Quiz next session you will get a stamp and a special award." Give students that scored 100% on the Homework Test, an award and a stamp today.

Material: TTTFW Workbook - Page 39

"TIMES TABLES THE FUN WAY"
WORKBOOK Lesson 6
HOW MANY FACTS DO YOU KNOW?
HOMEWORK QUIZ   QUIZ SCORE
correct: % score:

MISSED ON HOMEWORK TEST
_____ (previous pg.)
Name:
Date:

Write down the facts you missed on the Homework Test here. *Don't put the answer, just the fact.* Put one in each box:

Next session you will take this quiz and if you get 100%, you'll get a stamp.

Student Workbook Page 39

Topic:
Advancement Game

Goal:
To advance through each station by being the first to guess the fact. Winners end up at the Winner's Station.

Lesson 6

Set-up:

Select 4 captains to head each station. Put five 2 foot strips of masking tape on the rug to mark the four stations.

Material:

TTTFW Teacher's Manual - Page 88: Advancement Clue Card: 4 copies needed. Copy the cards on card stock and cut apart.

Rules:

1. If you win you move up to the next station. 2. If you lose you stay at your station but, go to the end of the shortest line. (see diagram)

Activity:

The class is divided into two groups, each group forming two lines at station one (4 lines total). The captain gives the first two people in line a clue, like "High Jump Contest". The first student to say 6 x 7 = 42 wins and may advance to station two. The loser goes back to the end of the line in his group, (station 1). The length of the lines will change so the loser should go to the end of the shortest line in his group. Play continues. When station two has enough players, the captain gives clues to the first persons in line. Again, the winner advances to station 3 and the loser goes to the end of the line. All stations play the game simulta-neously. A timer should be set to play the game for 15 minutes. At the end of 15 minutes give the winners, those who won at station 4, a Won Game stamp on their Stamp / Score Sheet.

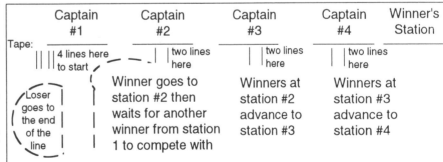

Game Layout

Captain #1   Captain #2   Captain #3   Captain #4   Winner's Station

Tape: 4 lines here to start | two lines here | two lines here | two lines here

Loser goes to the end of the line

Winner goes to station #2 then waits for another winner from station 1 to compete with

Winners at station #2 advance to station #3

Winners at station #3 advance to station #4

Whole class divides into four lines (classes of 20 or more, otherwise two lines at station 1 is sufficient to allow everyone to get equal play time.) Play Starts with captain 1. Captain 4 can help at station 1 until there are 4 people at station 4. When captain 4 leaves, station 1 reverts to two lines.

❖❖❖❖❖❖❖❖❖❖❖❖❖❖❖❖❖❖❖❖❖❖❖❖❖❖❖❖❖❖❖❖❖❖❖❖❖❖❖

Topic: <u>Issue Stamps</u>

Material: TTTFW Workbook: Score Sheet - Page 45

Activity: Students bring workbooks to the teacher so stamps can be issued.

Material: TTTFW Teacher's Manual: Awards

Page 98: Make copies and cut apart.

"TIMES TABLES THE FUN WAY"
Teacher's Manual

Section 7 - 1 *Two Quizzes And Nines For The Last Time*

Topic:
Homework Quiz...give 5 minutes to complete
Goal:
To score 100% on the quiz.
Activity:
Use *How Many Facts Do You Know* sheet that the students have filled out with the missed facts from the Homework Test. Tell the students to do their best. They will receive an award for scoring 100%.
Material:
TTTFW Workbook - Page 39

❖❖❖❖❖❖❖❖❖❖❖❖❖❖❖❖❖❖❖❖❖❖❖❖❖❖❖❖❖❖❖❖❖❖❖❖❖

Topic:
Grade Homework Quiz
Material:
TTTFW Workbook - Page 39
Activity:
When students have finished the quiz have them exchange workbooks and grade their quizzes. The Times Tables Answer Sheet can be copied and given to each student, or the quizzes can be individually graded by the teacher. When the quizzes are graded, have students that scored 100 % come up to receive their award and stamp on the Stamp / Score Sheet.
Material:
TTTFW Teacher's Manual Award: Page 98

❖❖❖❖❖❖❖❖❖❖❖❖❖❖❖❖❖❖❖❖❖❖❖❖❖❖❖❖❖❖❖❖❖❖❖❖❖

Topic:
Review Stories

Activity:
Ask for volunteers to tell the stories for:
8 x 3, 7 x 6, 8 x 4, 6 x 8, and 6 x 4.

Teacher's Notes:
_____
_____
_____
_____
_____

❖❖❖❖❖❖❖❖❖❖❖❖❖❖❖❖❖❖❖❖❖❖❖❖❖❖❖❖❖❖❖❖❖❖❖❖❖

"TIMES TABLES THE FUN WAY"
Teacher's Manual

Topic:

Quiz #6..give 5 minutes to complete

Goal:

Students will remember stories that go with the facts so that they can illustrate them. Give clues if necessary.

Activity:

"You will have five minutes to complete the quiz. You will not be recording your time so you don't have to try to hurry. Just try to finish it in five minutes."

Material:

TTTFW Workbook - Page 40

Answers:

TTTFW Teacher's Manual - Page 69

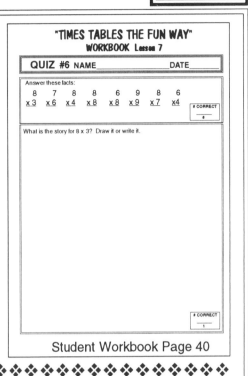

Student Workbook Page 40

Topic:

Nines Timed Practice Sheet

Goal:

To finish the sheet as fast as possible and still score 100%

Explanation:

"OK, now we are going to do the Nines Timed Practice Sheet for the last time. Try to get your best score and time ever. Be sure to go as fast as you can and try to beat your last time and score on the Nines Sheet. When you are done, write down your time and work on any of your unfinished workbook pages but don't work ahead of page 41. Everyone ready? Ok, You may begin."

Material:

TTTFW Workbook - Page 41

Student Workbook Page 41

"TIMES TABLES THE FUN WAY"
Teacher's Manual

Lesson 7

Topic:
Grading The Nines Practice Sheet
Material:
TTTFW Workbook - Page 41
Activity:
Class exchanges books and fills out Stamp / Score Sheet
Answers:
TTTFW Teacher's Manual - Page 75: Nines Grading Template

❖◆❖◆❖◆❖◆❖◆❖◆❖◆❖◆❖◆❖◆❖◆❖◆❖◆❖◆❖◆❖◆❖◆❖◆❖◆❖

Section 7 - 2   *Skill Check, Grab The Dinosaur, And Don't Say It*

Topic:
Worksheet #5
Goal:
This worksheet contains all of the skills that have been learned during the program. There is also a challenging story problem at the end of the worksheet. The goal is for students to be able to answer each type of problem.
Material:
TTTFW Workbook - Page 42
Activity:
Students complete worksheet while teacher gives individual help. Peer tutors can be assigned when finished with the worksheet.
Answers: TTTFW Teacher's Manual - Page 70

"TIMES TABLES THE FUN WAY"
WORKBOOK Lesson 7
Worksheet # 5

		Name two numbers that will give you this answer when they are multiplied together.
78 $\times 4$	88 $\times 3$	20 81
		36 25

Division:	What is your favorite story?
$5\overline{)25}$ $6\overline{)36}$	Why?
$4\overline{)24}$ $3\overline{)18}$	

Draw a picture of your favorite story here:	$7 \times 8 =$ $8 \times 8 =$ $7 \times 7 =$ $7 \times 6 =$

Story Problem: There was a boy named Pete. He had two mice for pets. Each mouse ate 25 cents worth of food each day. 1. How much did it cost Pete to feed his mice for a week?	2. How much did it cost to feed the mice for a month? (4 weeks)

Student Workbook Page 42

❖◆❖

Topic:
Game: Grab the Dinosaur

Goal:
If you know two factors for the number, grab the dinosaur, (stuffed animal), and say the factors. Tokens are awarded for correct answers. Winners will be the students with the most tokens.

Material:
TTTFW Teacher's Manual - Page 88: Grab the Dinosaur Factor Cards: Copy on card stock and cut out. One set is needed for each group. Also needed is a small stuffed animal to grab, like a dinosaur, one for each group.

Activity:
Divide class into groups of 4-5 students. Students sit in a circle. Teacher or captain says an answer like, 30. Student who knows two factors for 30 grabs the dinosaur, He then must say the factors immediately. If he fails to do so, or says them incorrectly, he must give up a token. He wins a token if he answers correctly. If the answer is incorrect, he puts the dinosaur back in the center of the circle and another student may grab it and give his answer. If a student says 6 x 5 for 30 and another student thinks he may have some different factors for the same answer, he can say "Dinosaur Bones" and then the answer. If he is correct, he gets two tokens and the student who gave the first answer gets one token. Students can not use 1's as factors. The students with the most tokens at the end of 10 minutes are the winners.Give winners a Won Game Stamp on the Stamp and Score Sheet.

❖❖❖

Topic:
Game: Don't Say It.

Goal:
Get your classmates to say the fact by guessing which story you are talking about. Be careful! Don't say the forbidden words.

Material:
TTTFW Teacher's Manual - Pages 89-96: Don't Say It Cards. Copy on card stock and cut apart. One set is needed for each group.

Activity:
Divide the class into groups of 10 or 15 students. Groups play separately. One player comes up in front of the group and tries to get the group members to say the fact that goes along with the clues. The teacher or captain holds the Don't

Lesson 7

Say It cards in front of the player. The card has the fact like 7 x 7 and some clues that the player can not say. The player can say anything but the words on the card. If he says a word on the card he loses a token. He gets one token for each card that the team guesses. Each team member that guesses the fact also gets a token. The captain or the teacher is the monitor to make sure they don't say the forbidden words. Each student has one minute to get through as many cards as possible. At the end of the game, students count their tokens. The four highest, win the game. Give winners a Won Game Stamp on the Stamp and Score Sheet.

❖❖❖❖❖❖❖❖❖❖❖❖❖❖❖❖❖❖❖❖❖❖❖❖❖❖❖❖❖❖❖❖❖❖❖❖

Topic:
Issue Stamps

Material:
TTTFW Workbook: Score Sheet - Page 45

Activity:
Students bring workbooks to the teacher so stamps can be issued.

Material:
TTTFW Teacher's Manual: Awards Pg. 98: Make copies and cut apart.

❖❖❖❖❖❖❖❖❖❖❖❖❖❖❖❖❖❖❖❖❖❖❖❖❖❖❖❖❖

Student Workbook Page 45

Teacher's Notes:
_____
_____
_____
_____
_____
_____
_____

Section 8 - 1 *Criss-Cross Words And The Rockin' Relay Race*

Topic:

Crossword Puzzle

Goal:

Fill in the crossword by remembering the stories for the facts. Some are easy and some are hard.

Activity:

The Crossword Puzzle can be played individually or as a game with teams. For team play, divide the class into groups of 5 or 6 students. Put a tally score card on the board. Give each team a point if they guess the correct word for the clue. Students can raise their hand if they know the answer. If the answer is correct, everyone fills in the correct crossword puzzle

"TIMES TABLES THE FUN WAY"
WORKBOOK Lesson 8
CROSSWORD PUZZLE

ACROSS	DOWN
1. 4 x 4 - ___	7. 6 x 8 Story	1. 7 x 7 Story	7. 7 x 8 Story
2. 6 x 7 Story	8. 6 x 3 Story	2. Camping House	8. 6 x 6 Story
3. 8 x 4 Story	9. A boy or	3. 8 x 3 Story	9. 7 x 6 - ___
___ pigs.	girl's name.	4. Grown up guy	10. 8 x 8 Story
4. 6 x 4 Story	10. 3 x 7 Story	5. When you're fin-	11. 2 x 6 - ___
5. 4 x 2 - ___	11. 3 x 3 Story	ished, you're ___	12. 3 x 4 Story
6. 7 x 4 Story	12. Opposite of no	6. Stop and ___	

Student Workbook Page 43

space. Teacher calls on the groups with the least points to encourage fair play. The group with the most correct guesses wins and may be issued a stamp on the Stamp / Score Sheet.

Material: TTTFW Workbook - Page 43

Answers: TTTFW Teacher's Manual - Page 71

❖❖❖❖❖❖❖❖❖❖❖❖❖❖❖❖❖❖❖❖❖❖❖❖❖❖❖❖❖❖❖❖❖❖

Topic:

Game: Flash Card Relay Race Game Two

Goal:

Be the first team to get through the complete stack of flash cards by answering them correctly.

Material:

Use two complete sets of *Times Tables The Fun Way* Flash Cards.

Activity:

Divide class in two even teams. Draw line on rug with masking tape. First student in line comes up and looks at the first card. He says the answer to the teacher. If he is correct, he writes the fact and the answer on the board and turns to the class and announces the fact and the answer. He runs back to his line and tags the next person in line who comes up and answers the next card.

The first team to get through the stack of cards is the winning team. Give them a stamp. Teacher leads one group and assistant the other group. If student doesn't know the answer, he tags the next student and goes to the end of the line. The next person comes up and tries to answer the same card. To make the game fair, group leaders, (with the cards) should stand at the same distance from the heads of the lines and don't show the card to the student until they have come to the front of the class. This game is played the same way as Flash Card Relay Race Game One. Refer to the diagram on page 15.

<u>Flash Card Relay Squares Game Variation</u>: Put two grids on the blackboard with 45 squares in each grid, one grid for each team. Instead of announcing the answer, students write the answer in a square. The first team to fill in all the squares wins. Don't forget to give winners a stamp on the Stamp / Score Sheet.

❖❖❖❖❖❖❖❖❖❖❖❖❖❖❖❖❖❖❖❖❖❖❖❖❖❖❖❖❖❖❖❖❖

Section 8 - 2   *A Perfect Post-test And Congratulations*

Topic:

Give Post-test...Time for 6 minutes

Goal:

The post-test is used to measure progress. It should be compared to the student's pre-test. Ideally, each student should score 100%.

Material:

TTTFW Workbook - Page 44

Explanation:

"You will be timed for 6 minutes, but this is not a race. Take your time and be sure to check your answers twice. If you get stuck on one problem just go ahead and come back to it. Be sure to do all the easy ones first, like the ones.

> ### "TIMES TABLES THE FUN WAY"
> #### WORKBOOK Lesson 8
> #### POST-TEST
>
> # correct: | % score:
> 48
>
> NAME _____ DATE _____ TIME _____
>
> | 2 | 3 | 4 | 3 | 7 | 8 | 1 | 2 |
> | x1 | x2 | x4 | x6 | x8 | x9 | x3 | x4 |
>
> | 5 | 6 | 8 | 9 | 1 | 2 | 5 | 6 |
> | x3 | x4 | x8 | x4 | x1 | x2 | x4 | x6 |
>
> | 9 | 6 | 7 | 2 | 4 | 5 | 5 | 8 |
> | x3 | x9 | x4 | x9 | x1 | x2 | x5 | x6 |
>
> | 9 | 5 | 9 | 1 | 0 | 3 | 6 | 6 |
> | x7 | x7 | x1 | x5 | x7 | x7 | x1 | x7 |
>
> | 8 | 9 | 3 | 5 | 4 | 8 | 7 | 3 |
> | x5 | x9 | x8 | x9 | x3 | x1 | x2 | x0 |
>
> | 7 | 1 | 2 | 8 | 5 | 0 | 3 | 2 |
> | x7 | x7 | x6 | x4 | x6 | x9 | x3 | x8 |
>
> Student Workbook Page 44

If you are finished before the time is up, just sit quietly and re-check your answers. If you score 100% on the post - test, you will receive an award, so please be accurate. The purpose of the test is to measure how much you have learned. Do you remember the very first test you had in the *Times Tables the*

Fun Way program? This is the same test, but I am sure that you will know more of the answers than you did the first time you took it. Be careful and make sure you have written the correct answer. Is everyone ready? OK, you may begin."

❖❖❖❖❖❖❖❖❖❖❖❖❖❖❖❖❖❖❖❖❖❖❖❖❖❖❖❖❖❖❖❖❖❖❖❖

Topic:
Grade Post-tests

Activity:
Students exchange workbooks while the teacher reads the answers. Graders should enter scores on the post-test sheet by entering the number correct. Percentages can be read to students.

Material:
TTTFW Workbook - Page 44

Second Chance:
The object of the program has been for the students to learn their times tables. Sometimes students write an incorrect answer even though they know the fact. For the students that miss 4 or less, you may choose to give each student one chance to say the answer. If the student immediately can answer you, you may mark it correct. This "second chance" approach is entirely optional but often eliminates some of the pressure that causes inaccuracy.

Answers: TTTFW Teacher's Manual
Page 76 Grading Template
TTTFW Teacher's Manual
Page 67 Percentage Scores based on 48 possible.

❖❖❖❖❖❖❖❖❖❖❖❖❖❖❖❖❖❖❖❖❖❖❖❖❖❖❖❖❖❖❖❖❖❖❖❖

Topic:
Issue Awards
Material:
TTTFW Teacher's Manual - Page 97: Awards for completion of program, (100% post test and congratulations)
Activity:
Issue awards to all students. Give stamps to students that scored 100%.

FLASH CARD NUMBERING SYSTEM

In order to easily sort cards for games and practice, the lesson number is entered onto the bottom right corner of each card. Here is a list of the facts and the corresponding numbers that appear in the corner.

<u>Lesson Number That</u>
<u>Appears in Corner</u>   <u>Corresponding Fact</u>

Number One: 1's, 2's, 3 x 3, 4 x 3, 8 x 8, 7 x 7
Number Two: 4 x 4, 7 x 8, 6 x 6, 5's, 6 x 4
Number Three: 6 x 3, 6 x 8, 9's
Number Four: 3 x 7, 7 x 4
Number Five: 6 x 7, 8 x 4
Number Six: 8 x 3

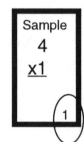

Review Table

Use this chart for a quick index to the stories and facts when review is needed:

Facts:	Text Pages:	Facts:	Text Pages:
Zeroes	16	6 x 7	56-57
Ones	23-24	6 x 8	48-49
Twos	26-27	7 x 3	52-53
3 x 3	30	7 x 4	54-55
3 x 4	31	7 x 7	58-59
4 x 4	34-35	7 x 8	66-67
Fives	38-39	8 x 3	62-63
6 x 3	42-43	8 x 4	64-65
6 x 4	44-45	8 x 8	68-69
6 x 6	46-47	Nines	72-81

"TIMES TABLES THE FUN WAY"
Teacher's Manual

PERCENTAGE SCORES

# Correct Total Possible: 48				# Correct Total Possible: 25		# Correct Total Possible: 24	
48	100%			25	100%	24	100%
47	98%			24	96%	23	96%
46	96%			23	92%	22	92%
45	94%			22	88%	21	88%
44	92%	19	40%	21	84%	20	83%
43	90%	18	38%	20	80%	19	79%
42	88%	17	35%	19	76%	18	75%
41	85%	16	33%	18	72%	17	71%
40	83%	15	31%	17	68%	16	67%
39	81%	14	29%	16	64%	15	63%
38	79%	13	27%	15	60%	14	58%
37	77%	12	25%	14	56%	13	54%
36	75%	11	23%	13	52%	12	50%
35	73%	10	21%	12	48%	11	46%
34	71%	9	19%	11	44%	10	42%
33	69%	8	17%	10	40%	9	38%
32	67%	7	15%	9	36%	8	33%
31	65%	6	13%	8	32%	7	29%
30	63%	5	10%	7	28%	6	25%
29	60%	4	8%	6	24%	5	21%
28	58%	3	6%	5	20%	4	17%
27	56%	2	4%	4	16%	3	13%
26	54%	1	2%	3	12%	2	8%
25	52%			2	8%	1	4%
24	50%			1	4%		
23	48%						
22	46%						
21	44%						
20	42%						

PERCENTAGE SCORES

# Correct Total Possible: 20		# Correct Total Possible: 19		# Correct Total Possible: 15	
20	100%	19	100%	15	100%
19	95%	18	95%	14	93%
18	90%	17	89%	13	87%
17	85%	16	84%	12	80%
16	80%	15	79%	11	73%
15	75%	14	74%	10	67%
14	70%	13	68%	9	60%
13	65%	12	63%	8	53%
12	60%	11	58%	7	47%
11	55%	10	53%	6	40%
10	50%	9	47%	5	33%
9	45%	8	42%	4	27%
8	40%	7	37%	3	20%
7	35%	6	32%	2	13%
6	30%	5	26%	1	7%
5	25%	4	21%		
4	20%	3	16%		
3	15%	2	11%		
2	10%	1	5%		
1	5%				

Correct
Total Possible: 11

11	100%
10	91%
9	82%
8	73%
7	64%
6	55%
5	45%
4	36%
3	27%
2	18%
1	9%

"TIMES TABLES THE FUN WAY"
Teacher's Manual

ANSWER KEY

QUIZZES

Quiz #1
9, 49, 12, 64
8 x 8: Snowmen
3 x 3: Mice
7 x 7: Soldiers
3 x 4: Cheer

Quiz #2
24, 16, 56, 36, 64,
49, 9, 12
6 x 4: Magic Pond
8 x 7: Bouncy Guy
4 x 4: Hang Glider
6 x 6: Thirsty Sixes

Quiz #3
18, 48, 25, 30, 81,
63, 40, 36
6 x 3: Hunter
6 x 8: Birthday
Cake

Quiz #4
21, 28, 48, 64, 49,
12, 16, 9
3 x 7: Butterfly
7 x 4: Fireman

Quiz #5
32, 42, 21, 28, 48, 18,
56, 24
7 x 6: High Jump
8 x 4: Dirty Pigs

**WORKBOOK
LEARNING PAGES**
Double Digit: page 7
35, 46, 126, 68, 48
29, 93, 96, 164, 186

Carrying: page 9
50, 72, 56, 154, 212

Carrying: page 10
372, 656, 126, 189, 275

Nines: page 18
63, 54, 27, 18, 9, 72, 63
72, 9, 54, 81, 63, 45, 36
27, 18, 27, 18, 45, 54, 81
63, 72, 18, 36, 45, 81, 72

Division: page 22
5, 4, 4, 6, 5, 7, 9, 8

Division: page 23
4, 4, 8, 8, 6

WORKSHEETS
Tens: page 11
22, 30, 36, 20, 11, 24, 50
60, 70, 72, 77, 99, 90, 48
12, 80, 88, 10, 66, 108, 40
96, 33, 44, 60, 55, 50, 24

#1: page 12
36, 44, 42, 99, 119
144, 34, 154, 132, 96
72, 72, 99, 108, 176
189, 224, 84, 50, 48

#1a: page 13
75, 180, 129, 156, 399
224, 94, 110, 128, 165
156, 132, 189, 396, 616
196, 216, 504, 260, 128

#1b: page 14
156, 220, 156, 260, 189
144, 116, 330, 64, 175
130, 132, 69, 366, 616
539, 224, 574, 360, 96

#2: page 24
276, 128, 336, 348, 108
384, 372, 126, 189, 440
6, 4, 6, 9, 7
6, 7, 8, 8, 8
7, 6, 3, 5, 3

"TIMES TABLES THE FUN WAY"
Teacher's Manual

ANSWER KEY

WORKSHEETS (cont.)

<u>#2a: page 25</u>
156, 168, 390, 520, 231
276, 108, 136, 329, 485
5, 4, 7, 5, 9
3, 3, 8, 6, 8
7, 7, 4, 9, 6

<u>#2b: page 26</u>
230, 208, 406, 448, 198
330, 156, 189, 385, 228
6, 7, 8, 8, 8
6, 3, 7, 9, 9
9, 9, 9, 3, 3

<u>#3: page 29</u>
282, 168, 162, 275, 184
196, 396, 290, 176, 320
365, 144, 98, 380, 410
7, 6, 3, 5, 6
7, 5
8, 5

<u>#3a: page 30</u>
392, 195, 192, 475, 384
156, 402, 425, 96, 275
185, 252, 111, 392, 112
8, 7, 9, 6, 3
7, 6
5, 7

<u>#3b: page 32</u>
268, 180, 132, 275, 276
231, 402, 290, 192, 456
312, 144, 108, 304, 410
4, 4, 7, 7, 3
8, 7
7, 8

<u>#4: page 35</u>
364, 385, 462, 352, 297
308, 231, 368, 98, 276
616, 624, 264, 399, 129
6, 7
9, 8

<u>#4a: page 36</u>
152, 385, 402, 392, 297
444, 161, 512, 198, 262
656, 312, 288, 406, 159
7, 5, 8, 6

<u>#4b: page 37</u>
252, 399, 522, 356, 147
188, 114, 562, 288, 230
644, 696, 260, 378, 147
8, 4
9, 8

<u>#5: page 42</u>
312, 264,
4x5, 9x9
4x9, 5x9
5, 6, 6, 6
56, 64, 49, 42
1. $3.50
2. $14.00

STORY QUIZ
<u>Story Quiz: page 31</u>
49, soldiers
42, high jump
64, snowmen
24, magic pond
36, thirsty sixes
48, birthday cake
21, butterfly
56, bouncy guy
32, dirty pigs
28, fireman
18, hunter

"TIMES TABLES THE FUN WAY"
Teacher's Manual

CROSSWORD PUZZLE

"TIMES TABLES THE FUN WAY"
Teacher's Manual

TIMES TABLES ANSWER SHEET

1 x 1 = 1	2 x 1 = 2	3 x 1 = 3
1 x 2 = 2	2 x 2 = 4	3 x 2 = 6
1 x 3 = 3	2 x 3 = 6	3 x 3 = 9
1 x 4 = 4	2 x 4 = 8	3 x 4 = 12
1 x 5 = 5	2 x 5 = 10	3 x 5 = 15
1 x 6 = 6	2 x 6 = 12	3 x 6 = 18
1 x 7 = 7	2 x 7 = 14	3 x 7 = 21
1 x 8 = 8	2 x 8 = 16	3 x 8 = 24
1 x 9 = 9	2 x 9 = 18	3 x 9 = 27
4 x 1 = 4	5 x 1 = 5	6 x 1 = 6
4 x 2 = 8	5 x 2 = 10	6 x 2 = 12
4 x 3 = 12	5 x 3 = 15	6 x 3 = 18
4 x 4 = 16	5 x 4 = 20	6 x 4 = 24
4 x 5 = 20	5 x 5 = 25	6 x 5 = 30
4 x 6 = 24	5 x 6 = 30	6 x 6 = 36
4 x 7 = 28	5 x 7 = 35	6 x 7 = 42
4 x 8 = 32	5 x 8 = 40	6 x 8 = 48
4 x 9 = 36	5 x 9 = 45	6 x 9 = 54
7 x 1 = 7	8 x 1 = 8	9 x 1 = 9
7 x 2 = 14	8 x 2 = 16	9 x 2 = 18
7 x 3 = 21	8 x 3 = 24	9 x 3 = 27
7 x 4 = 28	8 x 4 = 32	9 x 4 = 36
7 x 5 = 35	8 x 5 = 40	9 x 5 = 45
7 x 6 = 42	8 x 6 = 48	9 x 6 = 54
7 x 7 = 49	8 x 7 = 56	9 x 7 = 63
7 x 8 = 56	8 x 8 = 64	9 x 8 = 72
7 x 9 = 63	8 x 9 = 72	9 x 9 = 81

THIS PAGE MAY BE COPIED FOR CLASS-ROOM USE.

"TIMES TABLES THE FUN WAY"
Teacher's Manual
ONE'S AND TWO'S TIMED PRACTICE GRADING TEMPLATE

1 x 1	1 x 2	3 x 1	6 x 1

CUT EACH BLOCK OUT AND PLACE GRADING KEY OVER WORKBOOK PAGE FOR EASY GRADING

1	2	3	6
8 x 1	9 x 1	7 x 1	5 x 1

CUT OUT

8	9	7	5
1 x 4	2 x 2	5 x 2	2 x 6

CUT OUT

4	4	10	12
2 x 9	8 x 2	7 x 2	2 x 4

CUT OUT

18	16	14	8
2 x 3	3 x 3	4 x 3	497 x1

CUT OUT

6	9	12	497

THIS PAGE MAY BE COPIED FOR CLASS-ROOM USE.

"TIMES TABLES THE FUN WAY"
Teacher's Manual
FIVES TIMED PRACTICE
GRADING TEMPLATE

1 x 5	5 x 5	9 x 5	5 x 4

CUT EACH BLOCK OUT AND PLACE GRADING KEY
OVER WORKBOOK PAGE FOR EASY GRADING

5	25	45	20
6 x 5	4 x 5	8 x 5	5 x 3

CUT OUT

30	20	40	15
7 x 5	3 x 5	5 x 2	5 x 8

CUT OUT

35	15	10	40
5 x 1	5 x 9	5 x 6	5 x 7

CUT OUT

5	45	30	35
3 x 3	4 x 3	8 x 8	7 x 7

CUT OUT

9	12	64	49

THIS PAGE MAY BE COPIED FOR CLASS-ROOM USE.

"TIMES TABLES THE FUN WAY"
Teacher's Manual
NINES TIMED PRACTICE
GRADING TEMPLATE

9 x 5	8 x 9	4 x 9	9 x 9

CUT EACH BLOCK OUT AND PLACE GRADING KEY OVER WORKBOOK PAGE FOR EASY GRADING

45	**72**	**36**	**81**
3 x 9	6 x 9	9 x 7	9 x 1

CUT OUT

27	**54**	**63**	**9**
2 x 9	9 x 4	5 x 9	9 x 2

CUT OUT

18	**36**	**45**	**18**
9 x 8	9 x 6	7 x 9	9 x 3

CUT OUT

72	**54**	**63**	**27**
7 x 7	4 x 3	8 x 8	6 x4

CUT OUT

49	**12**	**64**	**24**

THIS PAGE MAY BE COPIED FOR CLASS-ROOM USE.

"TIMES TABLES THE FUN WAY"
Teacher's Manual
PRE-TEST / POST-TEST GRADING TEMPLATE

2 x1	3 x2	4 x4	3 x6	7 x8	8 x9	1 x3	2 x4

CUT EACH BLOCK OUT AND PLACE GRADING KEY
OVER WORKBOOK PAGE FOR EASY GRADING

2	6	16	18	56	72	3	8

CUT OUT

15	24	64	36	1	4	20	36

CUT OUT

27	54	28	18	4	10	25	48

CUT OUT

63	35	9	5	0	21	6	42

CUT OUT

40	81	24	35	12	8	14	0

CUT OUT

49	7	12	32	30	0	9	16

THIS PAGE MAY BE COPIED FOR CLASS-ROOM USE.

"TIMES TABLES THE FUN WAY"
Teacher's Manual
HOMEWORK TEST GRADING TEMPLATE

8 x8	7 x7	6 x4	8 x7	6 x6	4 x3	3 x3	4 x4	1 x1

CUT EACH BLOCK OUT AND PLACE GRADING KEY
OVER WORKBOOK PAGE FOR EASY GRADING

64	49	24	56	36	12	9	16	1

CUT OUT

2	6	8	4	18	10	5	4	3

CUT OUT

7	12	16	14	6	9	18	15	25

CUT OUT

35	45	40	30	20	18	48	21	28

CUT OUT

36	54	63	81	72	42	32	24	8

Name That Story Game 1	Name That Story Game 1
$\begin{array}{r} 8 \\ \times 8 \\ \hline \end{array}$	$\begin{array}{r} 6 \\ \times 6 \\ \hline \end{array}$
Name That Story Game 1	Name That Story Game 1
$\begin{array}{r} 7 \\ \times 7 \\ \hline \end{array}$	$\begin{array}{r} 8 \\ \times 7 \\ \hline \end{array}$

"TIMES TABLES THE FUN WAY" Teacher's Manual.....Game Cards

THIS PAGE MAY BE COPIED FOR CLASSROOM USE.

THIS PAGE MAY BE COPIED FOR CLASSROOM USE.

"TIMES TABLES THE FUN WAY" Teacher's Manual.....Game Cards

| Name That Story Game 1 |

$$6 \times 4$$

| Name That Story Game 1 |

$$4 \times 4$$

| Name That Story Game 1 |

$$4 \times 3$$

| Name That Story Game 1 |

$$3 \times 3$$

Name That Story Game 2	Name That Story Game 2
6 x4	4 x4

Name That Story Game 2	Name That Story Game 2
4 x3	8 x7

"TIMES TABLES THE FUN WAY" Teacher's Manual.....Game Cards

THIS PAGE MAY BE COPIED FOR CLASSROOM USE.

THIS PAGE MAY BE COPIED FOR CLASSROOM USE.

Name That Story Game 2

$$7 \times 7$$

Name That Story Game 2

$$6 \times 6$$

Name That Story Game 2

$$3 \times 7$$

Name That Story Game 2

$$7 \times 4$$

Name That Story Game 2	Name That Story Game 2
6 $\underline{\times 3}$	6 $\underline{\times 8}$
Name That Story Game 2	**Name That Story Game 2**
8 $\underline{\times 8}$	7 $\underline{\times 6}$

"TIMES TABLES THE FUN WAY" Teacher's Manual.....Game Cards

THIS PAGE MAY BE COPIED FOR CLASSROOM USE.

Name That Story Game 2	Name That Story Game 2
8 $\underline{\times 4}$	3 $\underline{\times 3}$

"TIMES TABLES THE FUN WAY" Teacher's Manual.....Game Cards

THIS PAGE MAY BE COPIED FOR CLASSROOM USE.

THIS PAGE MAY BE COPIED FOR CLASSROOM USE.

"TIMES TABLES THE FUN WAY" *Teacher's Manual.....Game Cards*

Pantomime Story Time
7 x7

Pantomime Story Time
6 x6

Pantomime Story Time
3 x7

Pantomime Story Time
7 x4

Pantomime Story Time	Pantomime Story Time
6 x4	4 x4
Pantomime Story Time	Pantomime Story Time
4 x3	8 x7

Pantomime Story Time	Pantomime Story Time
6 x3	6 x8
Pantomime Story Time	Pantomime Story Time
8 x8	7 x6

"TIMES TABLES THE FUN WAY" Teacher's Manual.....Game Cards

THIS PAGE MAY BE COPIED FOR CLASSROOM USE.

Pantomime Story Time	Pantomime Story Time
8 **x4**	**3** **x3**

Pantomime Story Time	Musical Fives Answers
3 **x8**	**5.....1 x 5** **10...2 x 5** **15...3 x 5** **20...4 x 5** **25...5 x 5** **30...6 x 5** **35...7 x 5** **40...8 x 5** **45...9 x 5** **50..10 x 5**

THIS PAGE MAY BE COPIED FOR CLASSROOM USE.

Advancement Clue Card	Grab The Dinosaur	
Mice 3 x 3 = 9	**6** 2 x 3	**20** 4 x 5
Butterfly and Tree 3 x 7 = 21	**16** 4 x 4 8 x 2	**28** 7 x 4
High Jump Contest 6 x 7 = 42	**24** 8 x 3 6 x 4	**27** 9 x 3
Break the Spell 6 x 8 = 48	**25** 5 x 5	**21** 3 x 7
Hunter 6 x 3 = 18	**15** 3 x 5	**54** 9 x 6
Cheer 3 x 4 = 12	**56** 8 x 7	**30** 6 x 5
Snail in Magic Pond 6 x 4 = 24	**72** 9 x 8	**35** 7 x 5
Mud Pies 8 x 4 = 32	**8** 4 x 2	**25** 5 x 5
Driver's License 4 x 4 = 16	**48** 6 x 8	**42** 6 x 7
Twins in Desert 6 x 6 = 36	**64** 8 x 8	**14** 2 x 7
Bouncy Guy 7 x 8 = 56	**63** 9 x 7	**40** 8 x 5
Two Snowmen 8 x 8 = 64	**36** 6 x 6 9 x 4	**81** 9 x 9
Army Guys 7 x 7 = 49	**10** 5 x 2	**45** 9 x 5
Fire Station 7 x 4 = 28		
King of Snakes 3 x 8 = 24		

THIS PAGE MAY BE COPIED FOR CLASSROOM USE.

THIS PAGE MAY BE COPIED FOR CLASSROOM USE.

Don't Say It Game Card

6 x 3

Hunter

Big Foot

Bow & Arrow

Forest

Don't Say It Game Card

7 x 7

Soldiers

Hole

Litter

America

THIS PAGE MAY BE COPIED FOR CLASSROOM USE.

Don't Say It Game Card

7 x 8

Bouncy

Trampoline

Diving Board

Pool

Don't Say It Game Card

6 x 8

Birthday Cake

Magic Spell

King

Castle

THIS PAGE MAY BE COPIED FOR CLASSROOM USE.

Don't Say It Game Card

6 x 6

Thirsty

Sixes

Desert

Hot

Don't Say It Game Card

8 x 8

Snowman

Camping

Fire

Sticks

THIS PAGE MAY BE COPIED FOR CLASSROOM USE.

Don't Say It Game Card

8 x 3

Bat

Cave

Snake

Throne

Don't Say It Game Card

8 x 4

Mud Pies

Rain

Bath Tub

Play

"TIMES TABLES THE FUN WAY" Teacher's Manual.....Game Cards

THIS PAGE MAY BE COPIED FOR CLASSROOM USE.

Don't Say It Game Card

3 x 7

Butterfly

Tree

Hatch

Cocoon

Don't Say It Game Card

7 x 6

High Jump

Skinny

Fat

Contest

THIS PAGE MAY BE COPIED FOR CLASSROOM USE.

Don't Say It Game Card

7 x 4

Too Late

Fire Station

Farmer

Barn

Don't Say It Game Card

6 x 4

Snail

Magic

Pond

Swan

THIS PAGE MAY BE COPIED FOR CLASSROOM USE.

Don't Say It Game Card

3 x 3

Mice

Babies

Tails

Blind

Don't Say It Game Card

3 x 4

Cheer

Yell

More

Math

Don't Say It Game Card

4 x 4

Hang Glider
Sixteen
Drive
Four Wheel

"TIMES TABLES THE FUN WAY" Teacher's Manual.....Game Cards

THIS PAGE MAY BE COPIED FOR CLASSROOM USE.

A PICTURE METHOD OF LEARNING THE MULTIPLICATION FACTS

Times Tables THE FUN WAY!

Congratulations to:

_____

I Scored 100% On My Post-test.
I Know All My Times Tables.

A PICTURE METHOD OF LEARNING THE MULTIPLICATION FACTS

Times Tables THE FUN WAY!

Congratulations to:

_____

For Outstanding Improvement
On My Times Tables Post-test

THIS PAGE MAY BE COPIED FOR CLASSROOM USE.

Congratulations to:

_____

I Earned 10 Stamps On My

Stamp And Score Sheet.

"TIMES TABLES THE FUN WAY" Teacher's Manual.....Awards

THIS PAGE MAY BE COPIED FOR CLASSROOM USE.

Congratulations to:

_____

I Scored 100% On My

Homework Quiz

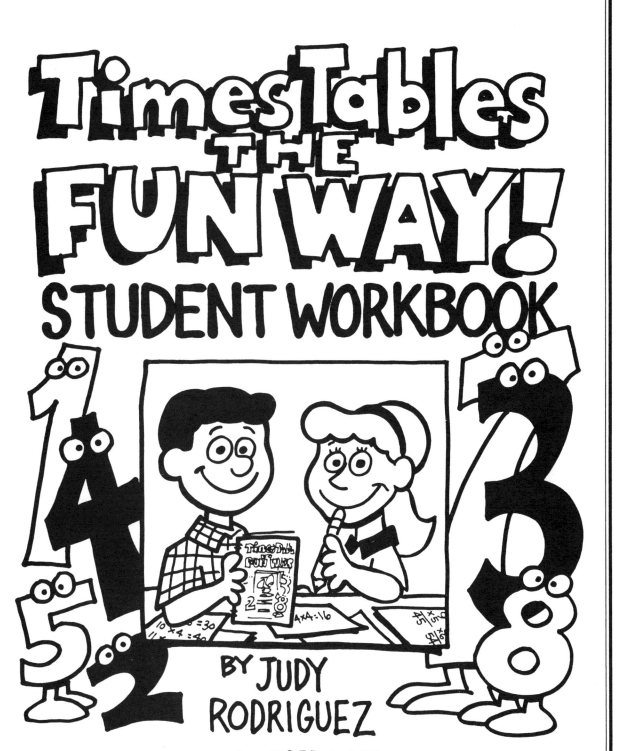

TimesTables THE FUN WAY! STUDENT WORKBOOK

BY JUDY RODRIGUEZ

TO BE USED WITH
"TIMES TABLES THE FUN WAY"
BOOK FOR KIDS

THIS PAGE MAY BE COPIED FOR CLASSROOM USE.

"TIMES TABLES THE FUN WAY"
WORKBOOK

STUDENT QUESTIONNAIRE

1. What is your full name?_____

2. Do you have a nick name? _____

3. What do you like best about school?

_____

4. What is your favorite subject? _____

5. What is your favorite food? _____

6. Do you have a pet, if so, what kind?

_____

7. If you could have one wish, any wish, what would it be?

_____

8. What are your favorite things to do? _____

_____

9. What do you want to be when you grow up?

_____

10. Name one thing that you are very proud of:

_____

THIS PAGE MAY BE COPIED FOR CLASSROOM USE.

"TIMES TABLES THE FUN WAY"
WORKBOOK Lesson 1
PRE-TEST

# correct:	% score:
――― 48	

NAME_____ DATE_____ TIME_____

2	3	4	3	7	8	1	2
x1	x2	x4	x6	x8	x9	x3	x4

5	6	8	9	1	2	5	6
x3	x4	x8	x4	x1	x2	x4	x6

9	6	7	2	4	5	5	8
x3	x9	x4	x9	x1	x2	x5	x6

9	5	9	1	0	3	6	6
x7	x7	x1	x5	x7	x7	x1	x7

8	9	3	5	4	8	7	3
x5	x9	x8	x9	x3	x1	x2	x0

7	1	2	8	5	0	3	2
x7	x7	x6	x4	x6	x9	x3	x8

THIS PAGE MAY BE COPIED FOR CLASSROOM USE.

"TIMES TABLES THE FUN WAY"
WORKBOOK Lesson 1
ONES AND TWOS TIMED PRACTICE

# correct:	% score:
___ 20	

NAME_____ DATE_____ TIME_____

1 x 1	1 x 2	3 x 1	6 x 1
8 x 1	9 x 1	7 x 1	5 x 1
1 x 4	2 x 2	5 x 2	2 x 6
2 x 9	8 x 2	7 x 2	2 x 4
2 x 3	3 x 3	4 x 3	497 x1

THIS PAGE MAY BE COPIED FOR CLASSROOM USE.

"TIMES TABLES THE FUN WAY"
WORKBOOK Lesson 2

QUIZ # 1   NAME_____DATE_____

Answer these facts:

$$3 \qquad 7 \qquad 3 \qquad 8$$
$$\underline{x\,3} \qquad \underline{x\,7} \qquad \underline{x\,4} \qquad \underline{x\,8}$$

CORRECT
___
4

What is the story for 8 x 8 ?
Draw it or write it.

CORRECT
___
1

What is the story for 3 x 3 ?
Draw it or write it.

CORRECT
___
1

What is the story for 7 x 7 ?
Draw it or write it.

CORRECT
___
1

What is the story for 3 x 4 ?
Draw it or write it.

CORRECT
___
1

THIS PAGE MAY BE COPIED FOR CLASSROOM USE.

# correct:	% score:
$\overline{20}$	

NAME_____DATE_____TIME_____

1 x 5	5 x 5	9 x 5	5 x 4
6 x 5	4 x 5	8 x 5	5 x 3
7 x 5	3 x 5	5 x 2	5 x 8
5 x 1	5 x 9	5 x 6	5 x 7
3 x 3	4 x 3	8 x 8	7 x 7

THIS PAGE MAY BE COPIED FOR CLASSROOM USE.

"TIMES TABLES THE FUN WAY"
WORKBOOK Lesson 2
LEARNING DOUBLE DIGIT MULTIPLICATION

Let's do one together , and then you'll be able to do it yourself.

First, ask yourself what is 4 x 2?

$$\begin{array}{r} 5\,4 \\ \times\,2 \\ \hline ? \end{array}$$

Right! the answer is 8.
   So, put the 8 right under the 2.

$$\begin{array}{r} 5\,4 \\ \times\,2 \\ \hline 8 \end{array}$$

Now ask yourself, what is 5 x 2?

$$\begin{array}{r} 5\,4 \\ \times\,2 \\ \hline ? \end{array}$$

Right, the answer is 10, so put the 10
with it's 0 right under the 5.

$$\begin{array}{r} 5\,4 \\ \times\,2 \\ \hline 1\,0\,8 \end{array}$$

The most important thing to learn is to keep your numbers lined up in very neat columns. This is important because it will help you get the right answer when you learn to do problems like: 54

                                                              x 54

Go on to the next page

     THIS PAGE MAY BE COPIED FOR CLASSROOM USE.

Now try this one yourself:

Ask yourself what is 2 x 3? Put your answer in the box:

```
6 3
x 2
```

Now ask yourself what is 6 x 2? Put your answer in the boxes to the left of your 6:

```
  6 3
  x 2
    6
```

Good Job ! Now try these:

```
3 5      2 3      4 2      3 4      2 4
x 1      x 2      x 3      x 2      x 2
```

You're doing great! Can you do these? Be sure to keep your columns straight.

```
29       31       32       41       43
x1       x3       x3       x4       x2
```

THIS PAGE MAY BE COPIED FOR CLASSROOM USE.

"TIMES TABLES THE FUN WAY"
WORKBOOK Lesson 2
LEARNING DOUBLE DIGIT MULTIPLICATION
WITH CARRYING

Let's do one together , and then you'll be able to do it yourself.

First, ask yourself what is 4 x 3?

$$\begin{array}{r} 5\ 4 \\ x\ 3 \\ \hline ? \end{array}$$

Right! The answer is 12.
But there is only one column for the 12, so you have to squeeze the 1 into its waiting place......

$$\begin{array}{r} {}^{1}5\ 4 \\ x\ 3 \\ \hline 2 \end{array}$$

Now ask yourself, what is 5 x 3?

$$\begin{array}{r} 5\ 4 \\ x\ 3 \\ \hline ? \end{array}$$

Right, the answer is 15, but before you write it you have to add the number in the waiting place, so ask yourself what is 15 + 1 ?

Right, 15 + 1 is 16. Now you can write the answer in its column.

$$\begin{array}{r} 5\ 4 \\ x\ 3 \\ \hline 1\ 6\ 2 \end{array}$$

Go on to the next page

THIS PAGE MAY BE COPIED FOR CLASSROOM USE.

Now try this one:

- -

Ask yourself what is 4 x 3? Write your answer:

$$
\begin{array}{r} 6\,3 \\ \times\,4 \\ \hline \end{array}
$$

- -

Now ask yourself what is 6 x 4?

$$
\begin{array}{r} 6\,3 \\ \times\,4 \\ \hline ? \end{array}
$$

- -

Ok, now keep the answer to 6 x 4 in your mind while you add the number from the waiting place.

Now write your answer.

$$
\begin{array}{r} 6\,3 \\ \times\,4 \\ \hline \end{array}
$$

Good Job ! Now try these:

$$
\begin{array}{r} 2\,5 \\ \times\,2 \\ \hline \end{array}
\qquad
\begin{array}{r} 3\,6 \\ \times\,2 \\ \hline \end{array}
\qquad
\begin{array}{r} 2\,8 \\ \times\,2 \\ \hline \end{array}
\qquad
\begin{array}{r} 2\,2 \\ \times\,7 \\ \hline \end{array}
\qquad
\begin{array}{r} 5\,3 \\ \times\,4 \\ \hline \end{array}
$$

Go on to the next page

THIS PAGE MAY BE COPIED FOR CLASSROOM USE.

"TIMES TABLES THE FUN WAY"
WORKBOOK Lesson 2

DOUBLE DIGIT WITH CARRYING *Page Three*

Excellent! Now try these: Be sure to keep your columns straight.

6 2	8 2	1 8	2 7	5 5
x 6	x 8	x 7	x 7	x 5

Now check your answers by turning to the back of the book. Then put your number correct here:

correct
———
22

Let's try doing some real easy stuff. Did you remember that zero times any number is always zero, because zero is the chief?

See if you can do these:

0	7	0	9	6	0	4	5	8	95
x1	x0	x8	x0	x0	x3	x0	x0	x0	x0

Wow! That was easy!

THIS PAGE MAY BE COPIED FOR CLASSROOM USE.

"TIMES TABLES THE FUN WAY"
WORKBOOK Lesson 2

TENS ELEVENS AND TWELVES

REMEMBER THAT ZERO TIMES ANY NUMBER IS ZERO.

11	10	12	10	11	12	10
x2	x3	x3	x2	x1	x2	x5

12	10	12	11	11	10	12
x5	x7	x6	x7	x9	x9	x4

12	10	11	10	11	12	10
x1	x8	x8	x1	x6	x9	x4

12	11	11	10	11	10	12
x8	x3	x4	x6	x5	x5	x2

Congratulations! Now you know how to figure out the tens, elevens, and twelves.

Go on to the next page

THIS PAGE MAY BE COPIED FOR CLASSROOM USE.

"TIMES TABLES THE FUN WAY"
WORKBOOK Lesson 2
WORKSHEET # 1

12 x3	11 x4	14 x3	33 x3	17 x7
18 x8	17 x2	22 x7	33 x4	32 x3
36 x2	24 x3	11 x9	12 x9	22 x8
27 x7	28 x8	12 x7	12 x5	12 x4

THIS PAGE MAY BE COPIED FOR CLASSROOM USE.

"TIMES TABLES THE FUN WAY"
WORKBOOK Lesson 2
WORKSHEET # 1a

25 x3	45 x4	43 x3	52 x3	57 x7
28 x8	47 x2	22 x5	32 x4	55 x3
78 x2	44 x3	21 x9	66 x6	77 x8
28 x7	27 x8	72 x7	52 x5	32 x4

THIS PAGE MAY BE COPIED FOR CLASSROOM USE.

"TIMES TABLES THE FUN WAY"
WORKBOOK Lesson 2
WORKSHEET # 1b

| 52 | 44 | 26 | 52 | 27 |
| x3 | x5 | x6 | x5 | x7 |

| 18 | 58 | 66 | 32 | 35 |
| x8 | x2 | x5 | x2 | x5 |

| 65 | 33 | 23 | 61 | 88 |
| x2 | x4 | x3 | x6 | x7 |

| 77 | 28 | 82 | 72 | 32 |
| x7 | x8 | x7 | x5 | x3 |

THIS PAGE MAY BE COPIED FOR CLASSROOM USE.

"TIMES TABLES THE FUN WAY"
WORKBOOK Lesson 3

QUIZ # 2   NAME_____DATE_____

Answer these facts:

6	4	8	6	8	7	3	4
x 4	x 4	x 7	x 6	x 8	x 7	x 3	x3

CORRECT
___
8

What is the story for 6 x 4 ?
Draw it or write it.

CORRECT
___
1

What is the story for 8 x 7 ?
Draw it or write it.

CORRECT
___
1

What is the story for 4 x 4 ?
Draw it or write it.

CORRECT
___
1

What is the story for 6 x 6 ?
Draw it or write it.

CORRECT
___
1

Page 15

THIS PAGE MAY BE COPIED FOR CLASSROOM USE.

"TIMES TABLES THE FUN WAY"
WORKBOOK Lesson 3
ONES AND TWOS TIMED PRACTICE

# correct:	% score:
20	

NAME_____ DATE_____ TIME_____

1 x 1	1 x 2	3 x 1	6 x 1
8 x 1	9 x 1	7 x 1	5 x 1
1 x 4	2 x 2	5 x 2	2 x 6
2 x 9	8 x 2	7 x 2	2 x 4
2 x 3	3 x 3	4 x 3	497 x1

THIS PAGE MAY BE COPIED FOR CLASSROOM USE.

LEARNING NINES

First, write down the number that is one less. Sample: What is one less than 5 ? Right! It's 4, so put a 4 in the blank | 5 _4_ |

3___   7___   8___   6___   4___   5___   9___   2___

Now, write down the number that you would add to make nine. Sample: | 3 _6_ | **Because 3 + 6 = 9.**

2___ 4___ 5___ 6___ 9___ 7___ 8___ 3___

On the next page, we will put these two steps together like this:

1. In the first space put the number that is one less than the number that nine is multiplied by:

Sample:

9	4
x3	**x9**
_2_	_3_

2. In the space with the double line put the number that you would add to make nine (2 + 7 = 9, 3 + 6 = 9):

Sample:

9	4
x3	**x9**
_2 7_	_3 6_

Go on to the next page

THIS PAGE MAY BE COPIED FOR CLASSROOM USE.

Be careful!! Sometimes the number that nine is multiplied by is on top and sometimes its on the bottom. Always use the number that is not the nine to figure out one less. (Except, of course, when it's 9 x 9.)

9	9	③	9	1	8	7
x7	x⑥	**x9**	x2	**x9**	**x9**	**x9**

one less   one less

6 3   ⑤ 4   ② 7

5 + 4 = 9   2 + 7 = 9

9	9	6	9	7	9	9
x8	x1	**x9**	**x9**	**x9**	x5	x4

9	9	3	2	5	9	9
x3	x2	**x9**	**x9**	**x9**	x6	**x9**

9	8	9	9	5	9	9
x7	**x9**	**x2**	**x4**	**x9**	**x9**	**x8**

Congratulations! Now you know your nines!

THIS PAGE MAY BE COPIED FOR CLASSROOM USE.

"TIMES TABLES THE FUN WAY"
WORKBOOK Lesson 3
NINES TIMED PRACTICE

# correct:	% score:
___ 20	

NAME_____DATE_____TIME_____

9 x 5	8 x 9	4 x 9	9 x 9
3 x 9	6 x9	9 x 7	9 x 1
2 x9	9 x 4	5 x 9	9 x 2
9 x 8	9 x 6	7 x 9	9 x 3
7 x7	4 x 3	8 x 8	6 x 4

THIS PAGE MAY BE COPIED FOR CLASSROOM USE.

"TIMES TABLES THE FUN WAY"
WORKBOOK Lesson 4

QUIZ # 3 NAME_____DATE_____

Answer these facts:

6	6	5	6	9	7	8	4
x 3	x 8	x 5	x 5	x 9	x 9	x 5	x9

 # CORRECT
____
8

What is the story for 6 x 3 ? Draw it or write it.

 # CORRECT
____
1

What is the story for 6 x 8 ? Draw it or write it.

 # CORRECT
____
1

THIS PAGE MAY BE COPIED FOR CLASSROOM USE.

"TIMES TABLES THE FUN WAY"
WORKBOOK Lesson 4
FIVES TIMED PRACTICE

NAME_____DATE_____TIME_____

1 x 5	5 x 5	9 x 5	5 x 4
6 x 5	4 x 5	8 x 5	5 x 3
7 x 5	3 x 5	5 x 2	5 x 8
5 x 1	5 x 9	5 x 6	5 x 7
3 x 3	4 x 3	8 x 8	7 x 7

THIS PAGE MAY BE COPIED FOR CLASSROOM USE.

Division is the opposite of multiplication. Here is a sample: 64 ÷ 8 = ?

Ask yourself what number times 8 will give you 64. Right! The answer is 8 because 8 x 8 = 64.

Here's another one: 56 ÷ 7 = ?
What number times 7 will give you 56?
Right! The answer is 8 because 7 x 8 = 56

Try these:

25 ÷ 5 = _____ (*Think:* **25 = 5 x ?**)
12 ÷ 3 = _____ (*Think:* **12 = 3 x ?**)
16 ÷ 4 = _____ (*Think:* **16 = 4 x ?**)
18 ÷ 3 = _____ (*Think:* **18 = 3 x ?**)
30 ÷ 6 = _____ (*Think:* **30 = 6 x ?**)
49 ÷ 7 = _____ (*Think:* **49 = 7 x ?**)
81 ÷ 9 = _____ (*Think:* **81 = 9 x ?**)
40 ÷ 5 = _____ (*Think:* **40 = 5 x ?**)

Go on to the next page

THIS PAGE MAY BE COPIED FOR CLASSROOM USE.

There is another way to write division problems. They look like this:

$$6\overline{)36}$$

When you see a problem like this, you ask yourself: What number times 6 equals 36, or 6 x ? = 36. The answer is 6 because 6 x 6 = 36. So, put the 6 on top of the house.

$$6\overline{)36}$$

Now try these:

$$4\overline{)16} \qquad 3\overline{)12} \qquad 5\overline{)40} \qquad 9\overline{)72} \qquad 3\overline{)18}$$

Go on to the next page

THIS PAGE MAY BE COPIED FOR CLASSROOM USE.

"TIMES TABLES THE FUN WAY"
WORKBOOK Lesson 4
WORKSHEET # 2

46 x6	16 x8	56 x6	58 x6	36 x3
64 x6	62 x6	18 x7	27 x7	88 x5

$6\overline{)36}$　　$3\overline{)12}$　　$8\overline{)48}$　　$9\overline{)81}$　　$8\overline{)56}$

$3\overline{)18}$　　$7\overline{)49}$　　$7\overline{)56}$　　$5\overline{)40}$　　$9\overline{)72}$

$9\overline{)63}$　　$9\overline{)54}$　　$9\overline{)27}$　　$5\overline{)25}$　　$6\overline{)18}$

THIS PAGE MAY BE COPIED FOR CLASSROOM USE.

"TIMES TABLES THE FUN WAY"
WORKBOOK Lesson 4
WORKSHEET # 2a

26	28	65	65	33
x6	x6	x6	x8	x7

46	27	17	47	97
x6	x4	x8	x7	x5

$6\overline{)30}$ $7\overline{)28}$ $8\overline{)56}$ $8\overline{)40}$ $8\overline{)72}$

$6\overline{)18}$ $4\overline{)12}$ $6\overline{)48}$ $6\overline{)36}$ $7\overline{)56}$

$3\overline{)21}$ $7\overline{)49}$ $9\overline{)36}$ $5\overline{)45}$ $3\overline{)18}$

THIS PAGE MAY BE COPIED FOR CLASSROOM USE.

"TIMES TABLES THE FUN WAY"
WORKBOOK Lesson 4
WORKSHEET # 2b

46	26	58	56	33
x5	x8	x7	x8	x6

66	26	27	55	38
x5	x6	x7	x7	x6

5)30   7)49   6)48   5)40   7)56

3)18   4)12   8)56   9)81   8)72

7)63   6)54   3)27   5)15   6)18

THIS PAGE MAY BE COPIED FOR CLASSROOM USE.

"TIMES TABLES THE FUN WAY"
WORKBOOK Lesson 5

Answer these facts:

3	7	6	8	7	4	4	3
x 7	x 4	x 8	x 8	x 7	x 3	x 4	x3

CORRECT
_____
8

What is the story for 3 x 7 ? Draw it or write it.

CORRECT
_____
1

What is the story for 7 x 4 ? Draw it or write it.

CORRECT
_____
1

THIS PAGE MAY BE COPIED FOR CLASSROOM USE.

"TIMES TABLES THE FUN WAY"
WORKBOOK Lesson 5
NINES TIMED PRACTICE

# correct:	% score:
$\overline{20}$	

NAME_____ DATE_____ TIME_____

9 x 5	8 x 9	4 x 9	9 x 9
3 x 9	6 x9	9 x 7	9 x 1
2 x9	9 x 4	5 x 9	9 x 2
9 x 8	9 x 6	7 x 9	9 x 3
7 x7	4 x 3	8 x 8	6 x 4

THIS PAGE MAY BE COPIED FOR CLASSROOM USE.

47 x6	56 x3	54 x3	55 x5	46 x4
28 x7	66 x6	58 x5	44 x4	64 x5
73 x5	36 x4	36 x3	76 x5	82 x5

$9\overline{)63}$ $9\overline{)54}$ $9\overline{)27}$ $5\overline{)25}$ $3\overline{)18}$

$21 \div 3 =$ $25 \div 5 =$

$56 \div 7 =$ $30 \div 6 =$

THIS PAGE MAY BE COPIED FOR CLASSROOM USE.

"TIMES TABLES THE FUN WAY"
WORKBOOK Lesson 5
WORKSHEET # 3a

56	65	24	95	64
x7	x3	x8	x5	x6

26	67	85	24	55
x6	x6	x5	x4	x5

37	63	37	56	28
x5	x4	x3	x7	x4

$$7\overline{)56} \qquad 6\overline{)42} \qquad 3\overline{)27} \qquad 5\overline{)30} \qquad 6\overline{)18}$$

$$21 \div 3 = \qquad\qquad 30 \div 5 =$$

$$45 \div 9 = \qquad\qquad 42 \div 6 =$$

THIS PAGE MAY BE COPIED FOR CLASSROOM USE.

"TIMES TABLES THE FUN WAY"
WORKBOOK Lesson 5

Stories

# correct:	% score:
$\frac{}{11}$	

STORY QUIZ Write the answer and one or two words about the story.

Facts

# correct:	% score:
$\frac{}{11}$	

ANSWER

1. 7 X 7 =

2. 6 X 7 =

3. 8 X 8 =

4. 6 X 4 =

5. 6 X 6 =

6. 6 X 8 =

7. 3 X 7 =

8. 8 X 7 =

9. 8 X 4 =

10. 7 X 4 =

11. 6 X 3 =

THIS PAGE MAY BE COPIED FOR CLASSROOM USE.

67	36	44	55	46
x4	x5	x3	x5	x6

33	67	58	48	67
x7	x6	x5	x4	x6

78	36	36	76	82
x4	x4	x3	x4	x5

$8\overline{)32}$ $7\overline{)28}$ $6\overline{)42}$ $3\overline{)21}$ $6\overline{)18}$

$32 \div 4 =$ $35 \div 5 =$

$56 \div 8 =$ $48 \div 6 =$

THIS PAGE MAY BE COPIED FOR CLASSROOM USE.

"TIMES TABLES THE FUN WAY"
WORKBOOK Lesson 6

QUIZ #5 NAME_____DATE_____

Answer these facts:

8	7	3	7	6	6	8	6
x 4	x 6	x 7	x 4	x 8	x 3	x 7	x4

CORRECT
____
8

What is the story for 7 x 6 ? Draw it or write it.

CORRECT
____
1

What is the story for 8 x 4 ? Draw it or write it.

CORRECT
____
1

THIS PAGE MAY BE COPIED FOR CLASSROOM USE.

"TIMES TABLES THE FUN WAY"
WORKBOOK Lesson 6
FIVES TIMED PRACTICE

# correct:	% score:
___ 20	

NAME_____DATE_____TIME_____

1 x 5	5 x 5	9 x 5	5 x 4
6 x 5	4 x 5	8 x 5	5 x 3
7 x 5	3 x 5	5 x 2	5 x 8
5 x 1	5 x 9	5 x 6	5 x 7
3 x 3	4 x 3	8 x 8	7 x 7

THIS PAGE MAY BE COPIED FOR CLASSROOM USE.

43	55	77	88	99
x8	x7	x6	x4	x3

77	33	46	36	46
x4	x7	x8	x3	x6

88	78	66	57	43
x7	x8	x4	x7	x3

$36 \div 6 =$ $35 \div 5 =$

$81 \div 9 =$ $48 \div 6 =$

THIS PAGE MAY BE COPIED FOR CLASSROOM USE.

38	77	67	98	33
x4	x5	x6	x4	x9

74	23	64	66	47
x6	x7	x8	x3	x6

82	39	72	58	53
x8	x8	x4	x7	x3

$63 \div 9 =$ $\qquad$ $35 \div 7 =$

$72 \div 9 =$ $\qquad$ $48 \div 8 =$

THIS PAGE MAY BE COPIED FOR CLASSROOM USE.

84	57	87	89	49
x3	x7	x6	x4	x3

47	38	69	96	46
x4	x3	x8	x3	x5

92	87	65	54	49
x7	x8	x4	x7	x3

$$48 \div 6 =$$

$$32 \div 8 =$$

$$72 \div 8 =$$

$$56 \div 7 =$$

THIS PAGE MAY BE COPIED FOR CLASSROOM USE.

"TIMES TABLES THE FUN WAY"
WORKBOOK Lesson 6
HOMEWORK TEST

Name:

Date:

8 x8	7 x7	6 x4	8 x7	6 x6	4 x3	3 x3	4 x4	1 x1
2 x1	3 x2	2 x4	2 x2	2 x9	5 x2	1 x5	4 x1	1 x3
1 x7	2 x6	2 x8	7 x2	6 x1	9 x1	2 x9	5 x3	5 x5
5 x7	5 x9	8 x5	5 x6	5 x4	6 x3	6 x8	3 x7	7 x4
9 x4	6 x9	9 x7	9 x9	9 x8	7 x6	8 x4	8 x3	1 x8

After you have taken this test and graded it, tear this sheet out and learn the missed facts for your homework assignment. Next session, you will have a quiz on the ones you missed.

THIS PAGE MAY BE COPIED FOR CLASSROOM USE.

"TIMES TABLES THE FUN WAY"
WORKBOOK Lesson 6

HOW MANY FACTS DO YOU KNOW?
HOMEWORK QUIZ

QUIZ SCORE

# correct:	% score:

# MISSED ON HOMEWORK TEST	Name:
_____(previous pg.)	Date:

Write down the facts you missed on the Homework Test here.
Don't put the answer, just the fact. Put one in each box:

Next session you will take this quiz and
if you get 100%, you'll get a stamp.

THIS PAGE MAY BE COPIED FOR CLASSROOM USE.

"TIMES TABLES THE FUN WAY"
WORKBOOK Lesson 7

QUIZ #6 NAME_____DATE_____

Answer these facts:

8	7	8	8	6	9	8	6
x 3	x 6	x 4	x 8	x 8	x 9	x 7	x4

 # CORRECT

_____
8

What is the story for 8 x 3? Draw it or write it.

 # CORRECT

_____
1

THIS PAGE MAY BE COPIED FOR CLASSROOM USE.

"TIMES TABLES THE FUN WAY"
WORKBOOK Lesson 7
NINES TIMED PRACTICE

# correct:	% score:
‾‾20	

NAME_____DATE_____TIME_____

9 x 5	8 x 9	4 x 9	9 x 9
3 x 9	6 x9	9 x 7	9 x 1
2 x9	9 x 4	5 x 9	9 x 2
9 x 8	9 x 6	7 x 9	9 x 3
7 x7	4 x 3	8 x 8	6 x 4

Page 41

THIS PAGE MAY BE COPIED FOR CLASSROOM USE.

"TIMES TABLES THE FUN WAY"
WORKBOOK Lesson 7
Worksheet # 5

78 88 x4 x3	Name two numbers that will give you this answer when they are multiplied together. 20 | 81 36 | 25
Division: 5 ⌐25 6 ⌐36 4 ⌐24 3 ⌐18	What is your favorite story? Why?
Draw a picture of your favorite story here:	$7 \times 8 =$ $8 \times 8 =$ $7 \times 7 =$ $7 \times 6 =$
Story Problem: There was a boy named Pete. He had two mice for pets. Each mouse ate 25 cents worth of food each day. 1. How much did it cost Pete to feed his mice for a week?	2. How much did it cost to feed the mice for a month? (4 weeks)

THIS PAGE MAY BE COPIED FOR CLASSROOM USE.

"TIMES TABLES THE FUN WAY"
WORKBOOK Lesson 8
CROSSWORD PUZZLE

ACROSS		DOWN	
1. 4 x 4 = _____	7. 6 x 8 Story	1. 7 x 7 Story	7. 7 x 8 Story
2. 6 x 7 Story	8. 6 x 3 Story	2. Camping House	8. 6 x 6 Story
3. 8 x 4 Story	9. A boy or	3. 8 x 3 Story	9. 7 x 5 = _____
_____ pigs.	girl's name.	4. Grown up guy	10. 8 x 8 Story
4. 6 x 4 Story	10. 3 x 7 Story	5. When you're fin-	11. 2 x 5 = _____
5. 4 x 2 = _____	11. 3 x 3 Story	ished, you're _____	12. 3 x 4 Story
6. 7 x 4 Story	12. Opposite of no	6. Stop and _____	

THIS PAGE MAY BE COPIED FOR CLASSROOM USE.

"TIMES TABLES THE FUN WAY"
WORKBOOK Lesson 8
POST-TEST

# correct:	% score:
48	

NAME_____DATE_____TIME_____

2	3	4	3	7	8	1	2
x1	x2	x4	x6	x8	x9	x3	x4

5	6	8	9	1	2	5	6
x3	x4	x8	x4	x1	x2	x4	x6

9	6	7	2	4	5	5	8
x3	x9	x4	x9	x1	x2	x5	x6

9	5	9	1	0	3	6	6
x7	x7	x1	x5	x7	x7	x1	x7

8	9	3	5	4	8	7	3
x5	x9	x8	x9	x3	x1	x2	x0

7	1	2	8	5	0	3	2
x7	x7	x6	x4	x6	x9	x3	x8

THIS PAGE MAY BE COPIED FOR CLASSROOM USE.

"TIMES TABLES THE FUN WAY"
STAMP AND SCORE SUMMARY SHEET

Lesson 1

Pre-test
Score: _____
Time: _____

1's & 2's Practice
Score: _____
Time: _____

Stamps:

100% 1's & 2's		

Lesson 2

Quiz # 1
Facts:_____Stories:_____

Fives Practice
Score: _____
Time: _____

Stamps:

100% Fives	Workbk. page 11	Workbk. page 12
Workbk. page 13	Workbk. page 14	Won Game
Won Game		

Lesson 3

Quiz # 2
Facts:_____Stories:_____

1's & 2's Practice
Score: _____
Time: _____

Nines Practice
Score: _____
Time: _____

Stamps:

100% 1's & 2's	Improved Score 1's & 2"s	Improved Time 1's & 2's
100% Nines	Workbk. page 17	Workbk. page 18
Won Game		

Lesson 4

Quiz # 3
Facts:_____Stories:_____

Fives Practice
Score: _____
Time: _____

Stamps:

100% Fives	Improved Score Fives	Improved Time Fives
Workbk. page 22 page 23	Workbk. page 24 page 25	Workbk. page 26
Won Game	Won Game	Won Game

Lesson 5

Quiz # 4
Facts:_____Stories:_____

Nines Practice
Score: _____
Time: _____

Story Quiz
Facts: ___Stories:____

Stamps:

100% Nines	Improved Score Nines	Improved Time Nines
Workbk. page 29	Workbk. page 30	Workbk. page 32
100% Story Quiz Stories	100% Story Quiz Facts	Won Game

Lesson 6

Quiz # 5
Facts:_____Stories:_____

Fives Practice
Score: _____
Time: _____

Stamps:

100% Fives	Improved Score Fives	Improved Time Fives
Workbk. page 35	Workbk. page 36	Workbk. page 37
100% Home- work Test	Won Game	Won Game

Lesson 7

Quiz # 6
Facts:_____Stories:_____

Homework Quiz:
Score: _____

Nines Practice
Score: _____
Time: _____

Stamps:

100% Nines	Improved Score Nines	Improved Time Nines
Workbk. page 42	100% Home- work Quiz	Returned Signed HW Test
Won Game	Won Game	

Lesson 8

Post-test
Score: _____
Time: _____

Stamps:

Workbk. page 43	100% Post-Test	Won Game

THIS PAGE MAY BE COPIED FOR CLASSROOM USE.

"TIMES TABLES THE FUN WAY"
Workbook
ANSWER SHEET

Ones and Twos Timed Practice

Row 1:	1	2	3	6
Row 2:	8	9	7	5
Row 3:	4	4	10	12
Row 4:	18	16	14	8
Row 5:	6	9	12	497

Fives Timed Practice

Row 1:	5	25	45	20
Row 2:	30	20	40	15
Row 3:	35	15	10	40
Row 4:	5	45	30	35
Row 5:	9	12	64	49

Nines Timed Practice

Row 1:	45	72	36	81
Row 2:	27	54	63	9
Row 3:	18	36	45	18
Row 4:	72	54	63	27
Row 5:	49	12	64	24

Pre-test and Post-test

Row 1:	2	6	16	18	56	72	3	8
Row 2:	15	24	64	36	1	4	20	36
Row 3:	27	54	28	18	4	10	25	48
Row 4:	63	35	9	5	0	21	6	42
Row 5:	40	81	24	45	12	8	14	0
Row 6:	49	7	12	32	30	0	9	16

Homework Test

Row 1:	64	49	24	56	36	12	9	16	1
Row 2:	2	6	8	4	18	10	5	4	3
Row 3:	7	12	16	14	6	9	18	15	25
Row 4:	35	45	40	30	20	18	48	21	28
Row 5:	36	54	63	81	72	42	32	24	8

Page 7

35	46	126	68	48
29	93	96	164	186

Page 9

50	72	56	154	212

Page 10

372	656	126	189	275

Page 22

5	4	4	6	5
7	9	8		

Page 23

4	4	8	8	6

Crossword Puzzle

Across

1. Sixteen
2. Highjump
3. Dirty
4. Magicpond
5. Eight
6. Fireman
7. Birthdaycake
8. Targetshoot
9. Casey
10. Cocoon
11. Mice
12. Yes

Down

1. Soldiers
2. Tent
3. Kingofsnakes
4. Man
5. Done
6. Go
7. Bouncyguy
8. Thirstysixes
9. Thirtyfive
10. Snowman
11. Ten
12. Cheer

THIS PAGE MAY BE COPIED FOR CLASSROOM USE.